1.50

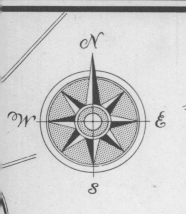

AQUA CLAUDIA

AQUA APPIA

HILL

in Way

ROME
1st Century

COPYRIGHT, MCMXLVIII, BY W. C. JENKINS

THE CHOICE • A STORY OF CHRISTIAN FAITH

The Choice

A STORY OF CHRISTIAN FAITH

BY Paul Sevier Minear

ILLUSTRATED BY HARRY T. FISK

The Westminster Press

PHILADELPHIA

Printed in the United States of America
at The Lakeside Press
R. R. Donnelley & Sons Company, Chicago
and Crawfordsville, Indiana

CONTENTS

Letter of Dedication...................................... 7

PART ONE · IN AN OLD WORLD

1   En route to Rome......................... 13
2   A Roman Home............................ 24
3   A Place of Prayer........................ 35
4   A Fisherman's Story...................... 45
5   A Dialogue............................... 54
6   A Dilemma................................ 65
7   An Arrest 75

PART TWO · TRANSITION

8   On the Appian Way........................ 87
9   Near the Fire............................ 102
10 Two Letters.............................. 115
11 The Price of Peace....................... 127
12 Herald of War............................ 138
13 The Peace of the Cross................... 149
14 A First Confession....................... 159

PART THREE · IN A NEW WORLD

15 Aftermath 173
16 A Narrow Road............................ 184
17 Another Narrow Road...................... 199
18 Giving and Forgiving..................... 208
19 Fear and Faith.......................... 221
20 Furrow's End............................ 236
21 Looking Backward 250
22 Tests of Love........................... 265
23 The Olive Tree.......................... 280
24 Waiting for the Spirit.................. 293
25 Crossroads 306

D*ear Larry:*

I have written this book for you, and it is dedicated to you in the hope that you will find it interesting and valuable. To be sure, others will also read it, but in telling the story my thoughts have focused not on many American young people but on a single reader—yourself.

You may ask why this should be so. This is the reason. Shortly before work on this book began, I had been engaged in drawing up a will. This task had set me thinking about your future. How can one person predict another's future? Who will you be several years hence? I do not, of course, mean the routine vital statistics that anyone can readily fill out, but those really vital statistics, the dimensions of that inner person who hides behind your words and your acts, that self who is the real you. No one can know just who you are and what you are meant to become. But this is the real you of the future, to whose growth I should like to contribute.

Then there is another thing. When that future arrives what will you want above everything else? More important, what will you need? Of course you will need money. One always does. But will that be your most urgent need? If not money, then perhaps I can leave you some real estate. But if bombs destroy the city, what value will real estate have? And just what is real *estate, that true possession which sustains a man in war or peace?*

Even if I could predict your needs accurately, how

7

can I supply resources for meeting them? A college training? Four years of college have been known to produce
less than the desired results. Instruction in the fine arts—
perhaps music and painting? Sometimes training in those
fields kills the joy of participation. Preparation for one of
the professions? How few young people today feel a really
impelling sense of vocation? Many people, it would seem,
are vocational misfits by the time they reach forty.

It's just as well that I can't solve these problems for
you. If I should try, you would resent my interference, and
rightly. At your age you feel competent to pilot your own
ship. You feel above restrictions and prejudices forced
upon you by older generations. You are eager to become
independent of the past and quick to rebel against inherited patterns of thought and action, whether at home,
at school, or in the Church.

I am grateful for this independence of yours. Though
you may not realize it, your freedom is a part of your inheritance, made possible in large part by the tradition of
the Church. However independent you may become in
the years that lie ahead, you will be truly free only if your
inner life is constantly nourished by the best of what we
treasure from the past—great music, great literature, great
faith.

So when I ask what you will need, there is only one
answer of which I can be confident. Whoever you will
be, and whatever you will want, you will need to claim
as your own the

"Life of ages, richly poured,
  Love of God, unspent and free,
  Flowing in the prophet's word
  And the people's liberty."

You will need to find yourself caught up in a continuing,
living relationship to God—the God of Abraham and the
God of Jesus. His life alone endures, his power alone is

8

adequate, his truth alone brings peace. The Bible is an emancipation proclamation that makes this peace accessible. It points the way to the only future that does not prove futile. And if you take that way, you will join a long procession of pilgrims and in that company you will share in the great prayers and hymns, rich liturgies and rituals by which the mysteries of the common life have been dramatically expressed.

This, then, is the legacy that I want most to share with you. And this explains my decision to address a book to a typical American youth, presenting to him Jesus' place in the Christian heritage.

It is not easy for one generation to transmit a legacy of this sort to the next. An ordinary legacy can be claimed simply by being the legal beneficiary. But the claiming of the Christian legacy is not so simple. It is offered as a gift, but to make it really yours you must strive with every nerve and muscle to become the person for whom it is intended. Faith cannot be transferred automatically from one to another. If you receive it, it will be at the deepest level of your own personal struggle to come to terms with life, when you commit yourself to the Father who has been seeking you through his Son.

You must do the choosing, but life's alternate roads are laid out in advance and are already well-traveled. How can I describe them so that you may know what the choice of Christ's way involves? Without dictating your decision can I show where some of these roads lead, as reported by those who have taken them? Perhaps the experience of another young man who learned the Christian way and entered into the legacy of Christ may be of help.

So I am going to tell the story of Clement, who lived in Rome nineteen centuries ago. There was such a man, and we still have a letter that he wrote about A.D. 95. From that year I am turning the clock back some thirty years

*and picturing him on his first trip to Rome, his first con-
tact with Christians, his reactions on first hearing about
Jesus' message, and the experiences through which he
discovered the meaning of discipleship. Many of the char-
acters, like Clement, are historical; some of the events are
fictional. Although much of it is imaginative, the whole
story is true to the life of Christians in Rome during the
first century, and true to the life of an individual as he
first came to know Jesus.*

*When Jesus enters a man's life, he opens up new roads
and thus transforms the future for him. We inherit his
legacy only by seeking first his Kingdom. And so to you
personally and 'to whom it may concern' I pass on this
inheritance. The Christian family is a very old one; its
treasures have been well guarded, and the accumulated
legacy is great. May it be yours to pass on with equal joy.*

PART ONE • IN AN OLD WORLD

CHAPTER 1

En Route to Rome

SOUTHWARD the narrow road pointed its slender finger toward Rome. On the left chattered the noisy Tiber, glinting through the trees in the autumn sunlight. Ahead loomed the contours of Mount Soracte, its eastern cliffs forming a white wall above the green woods. To the right of the road, olive orchards and vineyards were speckled with brown and gray shades of September. The cobblestone highway was quiet, for it was yet too early for the morning traffic from Rome to reach so far as this. It was an old and heavily used route, one that urgently needed repairs.

Toward the south trudged two travelers, matching their stride to each other and to the rough stones of the pavement. This was their third day of hiking, and their legs were stiff. Feet ached from the miles that had inched slowly by. Heavy packs chafed their shoulders. Clothes showed the effects of dust and rain; in fact, a close observer would have noticed straws from the friendly haystack into which they had snuggled last night. This morning their tongues were sluggish, and they made little effort at connected conversation, partly because travel fatigue still drugged their minds and partly because they knew each other so well. They were friends of such long standing that they needed no running dialogue to punctuate their stride.

At first sight, one would wonder what had drawn these two boys together, they were so different in face and manner. Julian was tall and loose-jointed, swinging along with easy grace and carefree gait. Quite at home in any company and in any situation, he appeared to be the leader of the two—aggressive, lighthearted, obviously content with life. He had a ready tongue and a flexibility of thought which quickly won the admiration of chance acquaintances. He did not demand too much of his friends, and gladly took the initiative in adjusting himself to their moods and minds.

Clement, by contrast, was stocky and swarthy. His face revealed his race; he was a Jew. And there was little to distinguish him from other Jews. Reserved in speech and in expression, he had been disciplined by life to shrink into the background. Shy and a bit awkward with his acquaintances, he was more adept at following than in taking the initiative. He never felt quite at home, never seemed quite content with a situation, never found at the right moment the right word for the lively banter in which his friends indulged. Although he appeared less flexible and less wiry than Julian, his body had the toughness of a hickory tree. His face was less finely chiseled, but his eyes were as alert and even more penetrating. His emotions were not visible on his face, and as a result some of his acquaintances thought him stodgy and dull. But those who knew him recognized that the deeper the feelings, the more they were concealed behind the mask of his stolid face. Of Julian it was true that his speech often outran his thought; of Clement it could be said that his thought usually outran his speech. While Julian would be occupied in noticing the river and the trees, Clement would busy himself with inward observations. The minds of the two companions moved at a different tempo even while their steps beat out the same rhythm.

On this occasion, as they began the last lap of the journey to Rome, Julian was absorbed in the beauties of river and mountain. Clement, keeping step automatically, was absorbed in a very different panorama. He was recalling scenes from his home which he had left two days earlier. And among all the scenes, his gaze gravitated to the colorful celebration of the New Year and the Day of Atonement.

As far back as he could remember, this celebration had been the high point in the year's calendar. Always his father had insisted that every member of the family be present for these "Days of Awe." He had even been stubborn in requiring that Clement delay this trip to Rome until after the holy days. At first this postponement had irked Clement, for a trip to the capital was something special. In spite of his disappointment, however, the mystery of the holy days had drawn him more than ever before, had quite magnetized his mind. Not that he could reduce the mystery into meaning or arrange its logic into neat links, but his mind kept mulling over the annual ritual.

Again he heard the blowing of the trumpet that ushered in the New Year. For it was written in the Law:

"And in the seventh month, on the first day of the month, ye shall have a holy convocation; ye shall do no servile work: it is a day of blowing of trumpets unto you."

According to his father, the New Year commemorated the first days of creation, and even God celebrated it by remembering the creatures he had made. The trumpet was the signal for God's examination to begin, when each year he tested men's faithfulness. On the results of this examination rested men's destinies during the coming year. Would their names be inscribed in the Book of Life or dropped from the roll of the faithful? Thus the day was an invitation for men to examine their own lives, and it was in such self-scrutiny that Clement's mind was now absorbed. What would be his special responsibility and his own fate during the year which had now begun?

In the midst of his reverie came interruptions. Once or twice his companion broke in with fragments of conversation: "How about stopping awhile to fish in the Tiber?" "These olive trees are more prosperous than ours." Such were the feelers by which Julian tried to revive the lively repartee of the previous day. But today Clement's answers were short and noncommittal. Even when Julian said, "Aren't you glad we don't have to plow that rocky field?" the reply he received was little more than an absent-minded grunt. It seemed impossible to pry Clement loose from his preoccupations. Julian noticed the curt answers, but wisely assigned them to harmless woolgathering and not to unfriendliness.

Clement, of course, would have relished the opportunity to talk over his groping thoughts about the New Year. But this he could not do with a Gentile, however warm the friendship. The first day of the seventh month meant nothing to Julian. On previous occasions Clement had been foolish enough to converse with Gentile friends about his family's religious ceremonies. But to his pain he had learned to be self-contained. Not only were his friends unable to understand these alien customs and attitudes;

worse than this, whenever Clement had mentioned some aspect of his life as a Hebrew, he had sensed a rising tension, a subtle shift of sentiments, an uneasiness of speech that blocked the flow of friendliness. Yes, he had learned, in a small degree, the barriers that divided his own people from the world. And although he could not fathom why the barriers should be there, he was grateful that a few friends were willing to ignore them. In some places the resentment against his race was bitter and unbending. How glad he was that his family had found quiet acceptance on Sabinus' plantation! How glad that he had found a few friends among his work mates!

Clement and Julian had many things in common. Because they were the same age, they had worked together and played together on the same plantation as long as either could remember. They had engaged in many tussles of wit and strength, the very tussles strengthening the bonds of their attachment. But there were certain lines which even their comradeship could not cross, and Clement had become painfully aware of them. One of these lines was marked out by the peculiar memories and hopes of the Jewish community. Clement realized that there could be no genuine sharing of the mysteries of the New Year. He must therefore keep sentry over his thoughts. The dialogue for which he yearned must be carried on within himself. Here was a private world into which even Julian could not come.

Each of us has a different calendar, he thought. *Our years begin on different days. To Julian, my New Year is simply like any other day, but to me it punctuates the text of life in a different way. Here an old sentence stops and a new one begins.* Suddenly he thought out loud, in a question:

"What year is this?"

Julian looked at his friend as if he were mad. "Why, the tenth year of Nero, of course. You know that as well as I do."

Clement was too deep in thought to notice the biting sarcasm. "Of course, I know that. But what year is it for us —not for Nero?" He meant this for himself, but the words were loud enough for Julian to hear.

"Are you out of your senses? Have you forgotten that we are the same age, twenty years?"

"No, I don't mean that kind of year at all," was the baffling rejoinder. Julian gave up any attempt to understand, and Clement drew back into the boundaries of his own private world. His thoughts rebounded to the scene at home.

His father and mother celebrated each New Year by repeating the stories about Abraham and Isaac. As a boy this had bothered him. Why repeat the stories of men who had lived so long ago and so far away? Four years ago —he remembered the occasion distinctly—he had been bold enough to protest:

"Why bring up such ancient memories to celebrate our New Year? What does the story of Isaac have to do with us?"

He could still see the shocked look on his father's face. "Aren't you a son of Abraham? If you are, then this story contains God's promise to you for this very year. His promise does not go out of date." Then his father had carefully repeated the story, as if it would provide its own answers.

God had promised to Abraham a son in whom all nations would be blessed. But only near the end of a long lifetime had this promise been fulfilled in the birth of Isaac. This belated birth had made his mother, Sarah, the object of derision. It had also been a source of conflict between Sarah and Abraham's other wife, Hagar. Hagar had jealously wanted her own son to inherit Abraham's legacy.

At God's order, Abraham had driven Hagar and her son into the wilderness. But in spite of this expulsion, God had protected her. And God had commanded Abraham to execute a most difficult and cruel duty, nothing less than to kill as a sacrifice his beloved son, Isaac. Abraham had based his hopes on the promise that in Isaac God would bless all nations. Now he must put this boy to death. Faithfully Abraham had prepared to carry out the order, taking Isaac into the hills and building the altar. Then, at the last moment, God had ended the ordeal by providing a ram to be sacrificed instead of Isaac.

"I still don't understand," Clement had stubbornly insisted. "What does that have to do with us in this New Year?"

Patiently his father had tried to explain, and fragments of his explanations still lingered in Clement's memory. "God fulfills our prayers, if we are faithful, but we must wait until he is ready. . . . God expects us to be willing to sacrifice our most cherished ambitions to prove our loyalty to him. God's purposes are not the same as ours. Our family may be destroyed, our hopes may be dashed, yet God has the power to carry out his purpose. . . . Only when we are as obedient as Abraham will we trust in God's promise."

This answer of his father had tantalized Clement. He had not understood all of it, and he had not liked what he understood. And each observance of the day brought back the same questions. At this most recent celebration, he had been provoked by the assurance which God had given Abraham:

"I will multiply thy descendants as the stars of the heavens. . . . In thy descendants all the nations of the world shall be blessed; because thou hast obeyed my voice."

Why doesn't God carry out this pledge? How long must we wait? Does God play with men, making promises and then breaking them, only to see if men will remain faithful? Is this the way in which God examines us each year, to see if we are willing to surrender all our hopes, simply because he demands it?

What a riddle! thought Clement. *Can it ever be solved? Perhaps God does not intend that we should solve it. Perhaps each New Year throughout his life, a man is faced with the same uncertainty.* As he mused, there came to him snatches of the hymn which his mother always sang on this holy day.

"My heart exults in the Lord;
 My strength is increased by him;
 I triumphed over my foes;
 Because I rejoice in thy salvation. . . .

"Boast no more so proudly;
 Be not so arrogant with your mouth;
 For the Lord is a God of knowledge,
 And by him actions are accounted. . . .

"The Lord slays and makes alive:
 He brings men near to death, and raises them.
 The Lord makes men poor, and makes men rich:
 He brings them low, and lifts them up. . . .

"For the pillars of the earth are the Lord's,
 And he has set the world upon them.
 He will guard the feet of his faithful;
 And will cut off the faithless in darkness."

The haunting cadence of the chant carried Clement back to the familiar atmosphere of his home. Although the New Year meant self-examination and penitence, it also seemed to lift his parents into a mood of sober joy. They might be quite uncertain of what would happen during the approaching year, yet the ritual brought them a peace of mind deeper than their anxieties. Others might think that the world was going to pieces; they remained confident that "the pillars of the earth are the Lord's."

But Clement was inclined to be more skeptical than they; he craved more tangible answers to the problems that faced him. *With Rome's power so irresistible,* he felt, *isn't such confidence in God too romantic and deceptive? Is it our God,* he wondered, *who makes some men rich and others poor? Does he guide all my steps, so that my future lies within the scope of his control?* He recalled the ardent assurance with which his mother sang the closing lines of the chant:

> " 'The Lord will judge the ends of the earth;
> He will give strength to his king,
> And exalt the power of his messiah.' "

That, he supposed, he must accept on faith, for its truth was certainly not apparent. Not now, at least. *What about Nero, with plenty of strength, but surely not God's choice? Who is the Messiah,* he asked himself, *whose power is to be exalted? There are no signs of his appearance. How, then, can my father and mother be so optimistic? Or why can't I be as confident as they? Is belief in God's salvation only a dream? If not, when will it come true? And what is the connection between that dream and my life during these coming months? What, indeed?*

Clement was brought out of his reverie by Julian's sharp question, "How soon do we eat?" For the first time he noticed that the sun was straight overhead and that he was beginning to be hungry. But his meditation still absorbed him, and he replied to his friend, "Let's wait until the road comes down to the river and we can eat on the next bridge." Julian gave abrupt assent, and Clement's mind shifted back to the old problem. Now, however, it took a different starting point.

Here is Julian, he thought. *Why should the Jewish dream place a barrier between us? We must eat from separate lunch boxes. I will say a benediction over mine. But he is free to say and do whatever he pleases. My family, my race, my religion, all place a wall between us which he cannot cross, and which I can cross only by cutting loose from my entire past. When he gets to Rome he will be free to look anywhere for work, to take advantage of every possibility. There is no limit to his social contacts, to his rapid advancement in whatever profession he may choose. Many of his new friends will despise me as a Jew. Will he stick by me, or will he join them in scorning me? What lies ahead of me in the city? Sharing the misfortune of a hated minority? The gates that are closed to them are also closed to me. And why? Chiefly because most of us Jews worship the God of Abraham and expect him to save us. If I surrender that hope, I can be as free, as happy, as confident as Julian. If I hold to that hope, I must pay dearly. What, then, does lie ahead of me?*

In this question, he realized suddenly, he had come back to the same point from which he had started. For the chief concern in the New Year was the destiny of each soul and each community during the coming year. *What is actually written in God's book for me and for my people? Each forward step implies knowing what lies ahead; yet the pilgrim can never know what he may meet around the next turn. Does God really have a purpose for me in every turning? And where lies the hidden goal?*

The road descended toward the Tiber, and Clement abandoned his reflections—and not without some pleasure, for he now realized that he was very hungry. The two companions opened their knapsacks on the bridge, and the monologue gave way to dialogue. Instinctively Clement tried to atone for his silence of the morning, and warm conversation repaired the ties of friendship that his inner absorption had strained.

A Roman Home

AFTER their lunch, the two companions walked with new eagerness toward the south, for they hoped to reach Rome before sunset. They marched briskly, though with curiosity, through the town of Falerii. They passed the inn where other travelers were stopping for a more sumptuous lunch than theirs had been. "I'm glad we don't have to sleep there tonight," remarked Julian. "They are said to house the largest roaches in Italy."

"Traveling is full of the unknown," replied Clement. "You can never be sure where you will sleep or what will happen next." His interest livened. "Shall we guess," he suggested, "what sort of party we'll meet next?"

Julian juggled several possibilities in his mind and then made his wager: a squadron of soldiers from the Imperial Guard. Clement's was a different prediction: a senator riding in a carriage, his slaves following with baggage, on

24

their way to a country estate. The boys did not have long to wait. Coming over the next hill they saw a single rider on a horse. Riding hard, an official courier with pouches of mail bore down on them. Stepping aside, they hailed him, hoping that he would stop to chat; but he galloped by without a word. His haste suggested some desperate urgency.

The boys renewed their guessing game, but more soberly. "We are so good at oracle-reading," ventured Clement, "what do you think will happen to us when we reach Rome?" He tried unsuccessfully to smother the note of deep concern. Julian sensed that beneath the words lay an anxiety not simply for the end of this journey, but also for what stands hidden behind all journeys. It was as if Clement had asked: "What is our future? How shall we go to meet the morrow?" And to such questions Julian would venture no guess.

For theirs was a time so turbulent that few could face the future with anything but half-concealed dread. Everything that had happened during this tenth year of the reign of Nero had intensified the people's fears. At first the emperor had been fairly popular, but no longer so. His name had become a byword which no one could use in public without fear of immediate reprisal. It was common knowledge that he had ordered his mother to be murdered, giving as an excuse the false charge that she had plotted to assassinate him. His wife, Octavia, he had falsely charged with adultery, as an excuse to divorce and banish her. Twelve days later he had replaced her by a much-married beauty, Poppaea, as dissipated as she was ambitious.

The emperor's path was not only paved with immoralities of this sort, but also lined with acts of sheer brutality and flagrant injustice. Opponents had been executed or exiled on the flimsiest of pretexts or on no pretext at all. Nero had refused to acknowledge the authority and influence of the Senate, and had discarded the steadying influence of trusted advisers, Burrus and Seneca. No one's life was safe. A poet had penned a piece of satire; immediately he was expelled and his property confiscated.

The private activities of the emperor were public scandal: lavish banquets from noon to midnight, gambling at the races with huge stakes, lewd performances in the theater, the attempt to substitute for traditional holidays and celebrations a full program of exhibitions and games imported from the Orient. Nero thought he was popular. And, it is true, he spent enough on public games and doles to keep the riffraff occupied and fed. This sort of popularity, however, merely inflamed the repressed animosity and dread among decent folk.

Dismay for the future was everywhere, and fear of things to come. Even the less superstitious had become alarmed when first there was a fiery comet, then a lightning bolt that struck the emperor's villa, then an earthquake that destroyed the Naples theater soon after Nero had left the stage. A resentful and harassed people quickly interpreted these as threats of divine displeasure. Yes, the tenth year of Nero had become a nightmare for most residents of Rome.

The emperor's unpopularity and the people's terror had reached a climax in the month of July in a catastrophe which was indirectly the reason for Clement's and Julian's trip to Rome. A fire had broken out in the Circus Maximus. Driven by brisk winds, it had spread beyond control through the very center of the city. For nine days the flames had fed on public buildings, business blocks, and rows of crowded tenements. The narrow, crooked streets had proved to be excellent flues for a furnace of destruction. Thousands perished with their homes; other thousands, fleeing in panic, were trapped in the narrow alleys. Hundreds attempted to rescue wealth or kinfolk and were lost. The aged and infants, invalids and prisoners, all were without chance of escape. During the days of terror, plunder and crime went unchecked. Many who survived were left homeless, hungry, and dazed. Those sections of the city that were spared were crowded with refugees.

It was to a world capital in ruins that Julian and Clement were hurrying. They had heard excited reports of the devastation and were eager to see for themselves what had happened. Fortunately, lodging and food in Rome had been arranged for them in advance. Clement would stay with friends in the Jewish quarter, which had been saved from the flames by the Tiber River. Julian would stay with other servants of Sabinus. Their first assignment was to restore one of the houses of the master in the burned-out section of the Esquiline hill.

Clement and Julian were freedmen of the household of Flavius Sabinus. Clement's father was an Asian Jew, who some forty years earlier had been brought to Rome as a prisoner of war and sold as a slave to the Flavian family. Julian's father had been brought from Macedonia, and because of his training had been made tutor to the children on the large estate. Working together on the plantation, the two boys had become close friends. Both had shown ability in carpentry and in mason's work, and because of this skill they had been called to Rome to aid in the reconstruction of Sabinus' city properties.

Being one of the city commissioners, Flavius Sabinus was now one of the busiest men in Rome. He had stayed in the city throughout the conflagration, and in the months since then he had been working without rest to restore order and a measure of security. The first job had been

one of erecting temporary huts for housing refugees, rushing in relief supplies, and setting up food depots in the
public parks and buildings. Then came the arduous business of clearing the rubble, opening the streets and aque-
ducts. Next came the repair of buildings only slightly
damaged, and the demolition of the empty shells of others.

Even while such relief measures were under way, the
emperor had hastily drawn up plans for a new Rome. He
wanted to make the main streets broad boulevards, lined
with spacious colonnades. Large blocks of rubble were set
aside for new parks, to be laid out and landscaped. A huge
new imperial palace would surpass all its predecessors.
The whole city was to be rebuilt on a magnificent scale.
Small wonder that Sabinus was busy with his labor bat-
talions, and that the citizens were just as busy with their
skeptical gossip! Why was Nero so energetic and such a
spendthrift in his plans? Was he trying to control discon-
tent by keeping everyone busy? Where could he find the
money to finance the reconstruction? Would he confiscate
the properties of unfriendly nobles as he had done so often
in the past? Had the emperor drawn up his plans for a
new city even before the fire? Was the fire a lucky accident or part of a devilish scheme to clear the ground for
the new buildings? Or was the fire a divine punishment
for neglecting the city's gods? Were the lavish expendi-
tures of Nero just a screen for covering his own guilt? or
simply his method of gaining fame in the eyes of posterity?

Before the ashes of the old Rome had cooled, animosity
against Nero flared up in new heat. Conspirators who had
sought for years to end the tyranny found a new chance to
gain recruits. Nero was busy forcing large "gifts" from
those who had money. And if a man failed to contribute,
his estate was confiscated. Officeholders were bled for donations. Those who were known to be hostile to the em-

peror were easy marks for exile or death. Nor did the
emperor hesitate to adopt inflationary schemes, lowering
the value of money in order to finance his projects. Here
was an emperor hated for his debaucheries and decep-
tions, a man who may have set fire to his own city, one
who pauperized those who were still wealthy and hounded
to death any who had the courage to oppose him. Of all
times, this was the moment for conspirators to strike. If
they could outwit their enemy and his bodyguard, they
would be hailed by the people as deliverers. But Nero was
not so stupid as to overlook this danger, and his secret
police combed the city for potential assassins.

This was the Rome that Clement and Julian entered
that evening. As they trudged through the impressive city
gate, they forgot their fatigue in the excitement of venturing into an unknown danger zone. As they approached
the center of the city they began to notice the ruins and
the signs of reconstruction. Clement stopped a man in
uniform:

"Can you tell us where we shall find the Street of the
Syrians?"

The officer showed his ignorance: "Do you know in
what part of the city?"

"West of the Tiber near the Janiculan hill."

"Oh, the Jewish quarter!" was the surly reply. He
scanned Clement's features with a sneer, as if to say:
"Another Jew! We don't want any more of them in Rome."
After a moment, however, he muttered, "Take the next
street on your right."

An ominous welcome, thought Clement uncomfortably.
Julian tried to pass over the insult by remarking, "They
seem to be suspicious of strangers."

Turning to the right, they soon crossed the river. Clement did not ask his way again until he came upon a man

who was clearly a Jew. This time he was met by greater
courtesy.

"That street is near the synagogue I attend. Whose
home are you looking for?"

"Bar-Joseph is the name."

"Oh, yes!" There was immediate recognition. "He is one
of the elders in the synagogue. Any friend of his is welcome among us. I know just where his house is."

The boys followed his directions and came with quick-
ened steps to their destination. Bar-Joseph met them at
the door.

"We have been expecting you all afternoon. . . . You
must be exhausted. . . . Here is your room. Supper will
be ready in half an hour."

The note of welcome was genuine. Julian, realizing that
the presence of a Gentile might complicate matters, suggested that he go on to Sabinus' house, but Bar-Joseph
would not consider it.

"Please don't think of it. It's too far across the city, and
you will get lost. And the police are sometimes rough with
the strangers they find on the streets after dark. No, you
belong right here tonight. Our fare is simple, but we really
want you to stay."

When their host had left the room, Julian expressed his
surprise: "What hospitality! He has never seen us before,
yet he takes us in as if we were members of his family."

"That's the rule with us," replied Clement, with a note
of pride. "All sons of Abraham are members of one family,
and we are taught to treat travelers as if they were brothers. Don't think twice about leaving. Bar-Joseph would be
deeply offended."

Soon they were called to supper, where they learned
that they were not the only guests. Three Jewish families,
driven from their homes by the fire, were sharing the

host's generosity. Into this circle the newcomers were quietly introduced and quickly accepted. The food was simple but ample, though both Julian and Clement were too keyed up to notice what they were eating. Julian felt too much like an outsider to talk freely. Clement tried to draw the refugees into conversation, but learned only a few facts about them. One family was now waiting the return of the father from Pompeii, where he had gone in search of work and a home. There was a family of weavers, whose shop had escaped destruction, and who were soon to move back into a remodeled tenement. Then there was a young couple, mourning the loss of two children. They were now constructing a new home in the western suburbs. All showed the scars of suffering and uncertainty, but in Bar-Joseph's home they relaxed in an atmosphere of assurance.

The travelers were too tired to continue the conversation after the evening prayers, and gratefully turned to their pallets. "I'm glad I stayed with you," Julian confessed sleepily. "This is so much more friendly than last night's haystack and the streets of Rome."

The following morning, Clement and Julian went promptly to the office of their master, the city commissioner. Not far from the Campus Martius they found his temporary headquarters in a shack at the edge of one of the new parks. Sabinus gave them their work assignments at once. First they were to help build a new city house for him on the Esquiline hill. They would work together. Clement would stay with Bar-Joseph across the Tiber; Julian would stay in the Esquiline quarters. Tools were issued, along with a sketch of the projected building. The materials had already been delivered, and by afternoon the boys were busy with the stone blocks.

Although they wasted no time, neither did they miss the opportunity to listen to the rumors circulating all

about them. They absorbed every detail, gradually forming their impressions of the situation. Clement was particularly struck by a tune that seemed to be on everyone's
lips. But he seemed to be unable to catch the words. After
some time, he asked another worker, who was whistling
the tune, what the words were. A harmless bit of dog-
gerel, to be sure:

> "Building Nero's city
> With vigor and joy,
> Building a future city
> That nothing can destroy."

Clement quickly learned the lines and began singing
them heartily as he worked.

During the day, however, it developed that other workers were using a different version. He slowly pieced it
together.

> "Who burned our fair city
> With hatred and glee?
> Do you want to know?
> Ask our leader, Nero."

Those who sang this version had the air of conspirators,
revealing a dangerous secret. This version was far from
harmless, for it carried the suggestion that Nero himself
was guilty. Clement noticed that this version was never
used in Sabinus' presence.

Once Julian heard Clement humming the tune, and
asked him if he knew what he was singing. Clement repeated the words. Then Julian told him a third version
that the workers were singing whenever Clement was not
present.

> "Who burned our fair city
> With hatred and glee?
> Let me whisper to you
> 'Twas an enemy Jew."

That spoiled the song for Clement, and spoiled the day as well. For now he noticed that when others whistled the tune, they looked at him with distaste, and he knew which version they had in mind.

Sabinus stopped late in the afternoon to see how things were moving. "How do you like your job, boys?" he asked the newcomers.

"Very well, sir," replied Julian.

"This is going to be a beautiful house." Clement was enthusiastic.

"Did you find your lodging satisfactory?" the master asked Clement.

"Just right."

"I hope you enjoy the city." Sabinus liked and trusted these two, and was sincere in his wish.

"It's very different from the country," replied Clement. "It may take me awhile to feel at home."

Sabinus understood what was troubling his worker. "Don't mind what they say about the Jews, Clement. They have to have someone to sneer at."

"But why should they accuse the Jews of starting the fire?"

"They see the big Jewish homes across the Tiber and are jealous that that section was spared."

"Last night I talked with three families who lost their homes in the fire; and one family lost two children. How can they blame us with burning our own homes?"

"Nothing but false rumors; yet these rumors can cause trouble. Some of them have heard stories of Jews carrying lighted torches. Some of them hate all foreigners and want to expel them from the city so that there will be more jobs for Romans. A few unpopular people have been mobbed; a few Jewish stores have been looted. I am sure, though, that you need not worry about yourself. You are safe on my property, and you have a good place to stay at night. You are so quiet and competent that none will molest you." With that the master dismissed the matter.

Clement, however, was not reassured. Filled with uneasiness over the whole situation, he found his way after the day's work to Bar-Joseph's home for the evening meal and the approaching Sabbath. Now he paid more attention to the refugees, and tried to draw from them their memories—a difficult task, for they seemed to want most of all to forget the nightmare of the fire and the hatreds of Roman hotheads.

CHAPTER 3

A Place of Prayer

WITH the sunrise the sleepers stirred slowly into the subdued activity of the Sabbath morning. Tired as they were, the refugees in the crowded house were all awake soon after the youngest child began his cry for food. The morning meal did not take long, for Bar-Joseph was eager to get to the synagogue to fulfill his responsibilities as an elder. Partly out of respect for him, his household and his guests all began the climb to the synagogue together. The Synagogue of the Olive Tree was among the largest in Rome, with a constituency of several hundred families. It was a simple but imposing structure, built high on the Janiculan hill overlooking the Tiber and the Campus Martius.

It was easy to see that those who gathered there were moved by something more than routine habit. Etched deeply in their faces were traces of constant anxiety. Their shoulders were bent with more than usual burdens. Yet they came with a calm expectancy of finding solace and strength. Silently they gathered, taking their seats with the absent-minded confidence of those who attend regularly, accustomed to receive a quiet blessing from the hearing of the Word. The men filed to the right, women to the left; while non-Jewish visitors climbed to the gallery. Clement was surprised to note the large number of Gentile guests in the gallery, seemingly intent on worshiping the God of Israel and on hearing his Word in the Law and the Prophets.

Even as a newcomer, Clement was quickly caught up by the surging tide of prayer. The worshipers filled even the silences with vigorous spiritual activity. No ornaments or actors were needed to unleash pent-up emotions and aspirations. Eyes were drawn toward the curtain behind which the sacred scrolls were kept. Eyes seemed to bore through the curtain, penetrating to that invisible place where each soul holds rendezvous with the Almighty.

The leader intoned the invitation to prayer with restrained dignity: " 'Bless ye the Lord, who is to be blessed.' " The response of the worshipers reverberated through the synagogue: " 'Blessed be the Lord, who is to be blessed forever and ever.' " Separate streams of thought flowed together as voices united in blessing their Creator.

" 'Blessed art thou, O Lord our God, King of the universe, who formest light and createst darkness; who makest peace and createst all things; who givest light . . . and in goodness renewest every day continually the work of creation. . . .' "

The voices gained momentum in this unison prayer, words dropping like pebbles worn smooth by the years. Each pebble as it dropped started ripples of mental asso-

ciations, circling out to distant shores of thought. One
such stone splashed into Clement's consciousness in the
phrase "King of the universe."

Yes, he thought, *that is the faith of my parents. But is
this God whom they worship actually the King? Is he the
only true God? If he is not actually King, how foolish and
futile to trust in him! But if he is the only true God, why
does it happen that there are so few who recognize his
authority? In what way does he maintain his rule over
such a confused and hate-ridden world?*

To these questions the next prayer came as a partial
answer, not wholly convincing to his mind, yet quietly reassuring to his spirit:

> " 'With great love thou hast loved us, O Lord our God;
> with great and overflowing pity hast thou pitied us. O our
> Father, our King, for our fathers' sake, who trusted in
> thee, and whom thou didst teach the statutes of life, be
> gracious unto us too, and teach us. . . . Unite our hearts
> to love and fear thy name, that we may never be put to
> confusion. . . .' "

From this prayer another pebble disturbed the pool of
consciousness: "for our fathers' sake." Perhaps he was a
bit homesick in this assembly of strangers; perhaps it was
the half-submerged memory of his father intoning this
same prayer; perhaps the sudden realization of his own
isolation in an alien world made him susceptible. Whatever was the reason, he suddenly had the overwhelming
impression that his own father was actually there in the
synagogue. Over there in that pew he could almost see
the familiar face. And through the gift of his imagination
he felt his father look at him, their eyes meeting in a shock
of sudden recognition. Every nerve in his body tingled.
"For our fathers' sake." Were the unseen parents of other

worshipers there too? and the parents' parents? He became aware that his life at this instant was linked into
their lives and that the whole chain of lives for many
generations was present now in prayer to the one Lord.

Now the congregation arose to repeat the declaration
of faith:

> " 'Hear, O Israel: the Lord our God is one Lord: and thou
> shalt love the Lord thy God with all thy heart, and with
> all thy soul, and with all thy might. And these words,
> which I command thee this day, shall be upon thy heart;
> and thou shalt teach them diligently to thy children, and
> shalt talk of them when thou sittest in thy house, and
> when thou walkest by the way. . . .' "

The voices rose and fell, blending into one chorus of
gratitude and commitment. Caught up in the stream of
common devotion, Clement felt that the weights on his
shoulders were being shifted. On the road to the synagogue he had been preoccupied with his own private
world. Like Atlas, he had been carrying on his shoulders
the load of his world. His mind had been obsessed by his
own worries and problems: What would these strangers
think of him? Would they accept him and increase his
happiness? What difficulties would confront him? How
would he make out among Gentile strangers? What friends
would he find in this turbulent city?

But the stimulus of group worship now lightened the
load by placing these problems in wider setting. Now he
realized that his small self was not the real center of
things. The world was a different place for every one of
these worshipers. Each of them, like himself, was an Atlas
carrying a world of cares and hopes. And to each person
that private world was important. Yet here in the house
of God all these pygmy worlds fused into one, a world
carried by all of them together. And the Lord God of

Israel carried the burden of all men. *To worship him,* thought Clement, *means to leave one's tiny world and to enter his huge world.*

Lifted out of himself into this larger universe of the Spirit, Clement heard the Shema as it continued:

"'Take heed to yourselves, lest your hearts be deceived, and you turn aside, and serve other gods, and worship them; and the anger of the Lord be kindled against you. . . . Remember all the commandments of the Lord and do them. Follow not after your own heart and your own eyes. . . . Be holy unto your God.'"

It seemed to Clement that this part of the ritual had been written for him alone, and for this very juncture in his life. Here was a sharp rebuke to his own inclination to chafe against the narrow customs of his people. One's heart and eyes were so easily attracted by the sports of the day, the glamour of popularity and prosperity. To be loyal to God in the daily activity of eating, working, and playing would increase the friction with Gentile employers and with people in general. To serve the God of Israel was the surest way to invite ridicule. As Clement already knew from brief observation, his faith might make him the target of hatreds that could provoke a riot on a moment's notice.

Never before in my life, he thought, *have I been so free to go my own way. In this huge city I can do as I please and shake off these connections with my race. But if I forfeit my membership in this community, I must face life entirely on my own, a straw tossed on the churning waves of current events. Is Rome like ancient Babel?* he wondered. *Has God confused their tongues, setting every man against his neighbor? Have the peoples of Rome, like ancient Egypt, been inflicted with plagues? But even though*

*our people are helpless in this mad world, where else shall
I find such fellowship as Israel provides, such power of
endurance?*

And so he saw the choice before him—to remain loyal to
his faith and retain his place among his own people, perhaps at great cost, or to select the freer and easier life of
the Roman, knowing that he would himself have to pay
the costs of that freedom. Today in Sabbath worship the
choice might be simple; tomorrow in his work among
pagans it would be more difficult.

After the prayers and benedictions were completed, the
head of the synagogue drew back the curtain and brought
the scroll of the Law to the reading desk. He then invited
Bar-Joseph to read the lessons for the day. As the congregation grew hushed in silent alertness, Bar-Joseph turned
to the fifth book of Moses. He read it first in the Hebrew,
then translated it verse by verse into Greek.

> " 'All of you are standing before the Lord your God . . .
> men of Israel, with your children, your wives, and the
> aliens working for you . . . that you may enter into
> covenant with the Lord your God, . . . that he may
> today make you his own people, that he may be your God
> according to his promise to your fathers, Abraham, Isaac,
> and Jacob. . . . I make this covenant both with you who
> are standing here today, and with those who are not here
> with us today.' "

Here Bar-Joseph turned his eyes to the gallery and
accented the words in such a way as to make the Gentile
visitors aware of an invitation to join their Jewish neighbors in this covenant, an invitation which God had himself
proffered. Bar-Joseph knew why various outsiders had
been drawn to the fringe of faith. Some had been impressed by the antiquity of this sacred writing; some had
been drawn by the unity and purity of this God; some had

sensed a fellowship among this people which was not to
be found elsewhere. Bar-Joseph wanted them to know
that what might seem to be exclusiveness and stubbornness on the part of the Jews was due, not to human pride,
but to the righteous demands of God, who placed upon
members of the covenant even heavier requirements than
upon outsiders.

The reading from Moses left little doubt of the rigorous
character of God's claims upon his servants. Gall and
wormwood would grow in the heart of the truant, and because of the stubbornness of his heart God would curse
him and blot his name out of the heavenly scroll. Yet men
always could return to the covenant and inherit the promises that the God of the covenant offered:

> " 'When the blessings and the curses have overtaken you,
> when you call them to mind among the nations, where
> God has scattered you, when you return to the Lord your
> God, and serve him with all your heart, then God will
> take pity on you. He will restore your fortune. He will
> gather you again from all the nations. He will bring you
> back to the land which your fathers possessed. . . . He
> will give you a new heart to love him, that you may live.' "

This promise of a happy return one day to Palestine
divided the congregation into two groups, according to
their backgrounds. Those who had come recently from the
homeland, and whose hearts lingered there, pictured again
the towers of the holy city. In imagination they were again
in the Temple at Jerusalem, bringing their sacrifices and
singing their hymns. Through the corridors of their minds
raced the evil rumors which they had been hearing. The
men of Jerusalem had clashed with Roman troops. . . .
Patriots had raised the flag of revolt and had refused to
pay the taxes. . . . A small contingent of Roman soldiers

had been ambushed. . . . At Passover of the preceding year human blood had been shed in the Temple itself. War might break out at any moment, as a scourge of God on evil men. It was against such a background that they heard God's pledge of returning peace.

A large number of the worshipers, however, were more concerned over the immediate prospect in Rome. Here was their home, their heart, their destiny. Here, too, God's promise seemed to be contradicted by fact. Any night might bring mobs surging into their quarter to wreck their homes. Any day might mark a sudden lynching in the market place. War in Judea might well bring on a purge in Rome, releasing all restraints against anti-Semitism. Israelites throughout the empire—and there were more of them outside than inside the Holy Land—might be treated as traitors who had forfeited all rights to protection under the law.

To all appearances Israel was cursed and her enemies blessed. Yet the Scripture assured the faithful that their only hope was in their God and in fidelity to his Law. As one of their teachers had said: "If all Israel will obey the Law wholly for as long as a single Sabbath day, God will establish his Kingdom and fulfill his promise." Set over against this pledge echoed the constant gibes of the skeptic, heard since the day of the psalmist: "Where is now thy God?" While the worshipers' minds were thus engaged, Bar-Joseph continued his reading, first in Hebrew and then translating it into the language of the people. Because few could understand the original language, the reading in Hebrew gave alert minds ample time for mulling over the implications of the previous verses.

Now the reader turned from the Law to the Prophets. Here the selection for the day was the prophecy of Jeremiah. As in the reading from Moses, so the words of

Jeremiah alternated between a sharp accusation of sin and
a strong assurance of coming forgiveness. Bar-Joseph read
slowly so that each word rang in Clement's ears:

> " 'Your wound is incurable,
>   Your sickness is far advanced.
>   No medicine is there for your wound:
>   No healing for your sickness.
>   Your friends have forgotten you;
>   They care no more for you:
>   For I have dealt you an enemy's blow,
>   The punishment of a cruel foe,
>   Because your guilt is great,
>   And your sins are flagrant.' "

Yes, we have broken God's covenant, thought Clement.
*We have sinned, with our fathers. Our suffering is God's
righteous punishment. But how have we sinned? We must
know our sin before we ask forgiveness for it. In what
ways have we broken the covenant? Will God reveal to
us the character of our rebellion? Otherwise, how can we
fully repent?*

The reading continued with the proclamation of God's
forgiveness:

> " 'I will bring you recovery,
>   And will heal your wounds. . . .
>   I am restoring the tents of Jacob,
>   And will have pity on his homes. . . .
>   Your ruler shall come from among you;
>   And I will cause him to draw near to me . . .
>   And you shall be my people,
>   And I will be your God.' "

Yes, came the unspoken response of the people. *Yes, we
need forgiveness and recovery. And only God can heal and
save us. Only he can draw scattered exiles back to our
true homeland. He will restore our nation and establish it*

*forever. He has promised. Let Israel obey. Let Israel re-
member in gratitude the former deliverances. Let Israel
wait in patient expectancy the coming miracle of a new
heart, a new people, a new age. Let Israel be patient, let
us repent, let us be faithful to our holy institutions.*

Such were the responses woven into the sober amens
with which the congregation replied to the ending of the
reading. After the prayers and benedictions, the people
dispersed. One by one they closed the doors of their
minds, hiding from the world the thoughts which a moment before had been open to God. Young people remained in the building for regular instruction in the Law.
The older people left, but many loitered in the porch to
exchange greetings and gossip. Clement was eager to get
away to a secluded place where he could rethink the impressions that had been racing through his head. This
desire, however, was not to be fulfilled immediately.

CHAPTER 4

A Fisherman's Story

NEAR one corner of the synagogue porch Clement noticed a number of worshipers gathered in animated argument. They clustered about a man who was addressing all who would listen. He was short and swarthy, with that complexion that comes from years of work out of doors. He looked like a sailor or a peasant, though he acted with quiet self-assurance and a poise that made it difficult to tell whether he was an experienced traveler or a long-time resident here. His face reflected a self-forgetful absorption in his message, and he spoke with utter frankness and an open genuineness that set him apart from the usual street-corner haranguer. Here was no demagogue appealing for personal support or profit, but one whose voice carried the accent of deep conviction and personal enthusiasm.

Clement heard: "The Scripture has been fulfilled. God has chosen to carry out his promise."

"What Scripture do you mean?" a bystander asked.

"The Law and the Prophets which you have just heard," replied the speaker. "The promise of a new day and a new covenant." Clement noticed a slight movement on the opposite side of the group and saw Bar-Joseph edging closer to hear. Recognizing him, the speaker continued, "Your elder read how Moses announced that God would send a new prophet and create a new people, according to the agreement which he made with our fathers."

"Your elder, our fathers." He must be a newcomer in this synagogue, and a Jew, thought Clement.

"Do you mean that Gentiles will have a place in the new day that is coming?" Bar-Joseph's question was edged with opposition.

"Such is the promise as you read it from the Law." Several in the group, obviously Gentiles, welcomed this ready response. "The Law also says," continued the stranger, "that our sin is greater than the sin of the other nations. It is among the sons of Abraham that God finds the most flagrant refusal to do his will. God will curse those whose hearts stubbornly resist his purposes. He will blot out their names, separating them for special punishment. For though they think that they worship him, in blindness they actually serve false gods."

A wave of muttering surged through the group. "Are we then more guilty than the Gentiles—we who have endured so much hatred for God's sake?"

"Read the Law and the Prophets," came the reply of the stranger. "Has not God given more grace to our community than to others? Has he not charged us with greater responsibility? From the days in Egypt until today has not Israel constantly rebelled against God? We have the

Law. Yes, but we have prided ourselves on it as our own possession. We have memorized the commands of God, but we have complacently trusted in our own righteousness. We have seen God's wrath executed in every generation. Yes, but we have hoped to claim exemptions for ourselves. And all the while we have looked down upon Gentiles as chief among sinners.

"Yet in spite of our unfaithfulness God has remained faithful and he will keep his pledge. To Moses and Jeremiah he promised a deliverer. He assured them that he would raise up a new prophet and a new people to accomplish his purposes." He paused and then cried out with dramatic intensity: "God has at last acted to save us. He has sent his Messiah. The ages of agony are over. The new age has begun."

Astonished and puzzled, the listeners buzzed with questions: "When did this happen?" "Who is the Messiah?" "Where is he?" "Where is this Kingdom? So far as we have heard, nothing has happened." Looking about him, Clement saw faces filled with conflicting emotions: bewilderment, incredulity, curiosity, antagonism. *What an unbelievable message! Is the man crazy? How can anyone confuse this present situation with the Kingdom of God? Is this man calling for armed violence against Rome?*

"Your very questions show how sin has blinded your eyes," the speaker went on in spite of the buzz of voices. "You want a powerful king who will destroy all outsiders. You want a reformer who will provide you with wealth and comfort. You want a messiah who will compel everyone to believe in him by spectacular deeds. And unless you see such a miracle you refuse to believe. You actually do not consider it possible for God to bring his Kingdom near to us here in Rome, now in this time of calamity.

"But don't decide too hastily. Hear my news and then

decide for yourselves." The stranger spoke clearly and with great earnestness. "Not long ago there arose in Judea a prophet whose name was John. We had supposed the days of the prophets were over. No, they have come again. Like Elijah, John came from the wilderness to the Jordan, driven by God's spirit to warn men of coming judgment. I myself heard him shout: 'The fires of God's final judgment are already burning. The day of redemption is at hand. If you want to be saved for life in the new age, you must repent and be baptized. The fact that you are a son of Abraham won't help you unless you forsake the present age and seek to enter the dawning age.'

"That was John's message. And what happened to him? Though many of us accepted his warning, most of our people refused to hear his voice. And Herod, our king, in great alarm arrested him and later beheaded him. But John had opened the road for one greater than he. God sent the Messiah himself in the person of Jesus of Galilee. He came from the family of David in the town of Nazareth."

"A strange place for the Messiah to come from," someone muttered.

"Who are we, to tell God how to save us?" was the speaker's instant rebuttal. "And you may be sure," he continued, "that the Galileans were as skeptical as you Romans. They could not believe such things about one of their own neighbors. I know, because I was there. After John had been thrown into Herod's fortress I returned to Capernaum, where I earned my living by fishing. One day I heard that this carpenter from Nazareth had arrived in the neighborhood. I was drawn to him immediately because he was proclaiming the same warning as John.

"But there was something more exciting than simply the threat of doom. Strange things happened to those who repented at his preaching. He announced that God was al-

ready forgiving their sins and healing their wounds. Final
victory was now within man's reach."

The speaker's voice dropped to a more intimate tone.
His eyes were fixed far away, as if he were again in Capernaum, seeing for the first time the scenes he was describing.

"I wish I could tell you all the things that actually happened when this carpenter came to town. He spoke of
God as though he were right there in our midst, where
we had never thought of looking: in the street, on the
beach, in the sickroom, in the market place.

"He acted as if a man could trust God completely to
provide everything a person needs. In him there was no
trace of hurry or anger or fear. He radiated such peace and
joy that in his presence sick people were made well. My
own mother-in-law was cured. People who were crazy
with pain and despair became quiet and confident. Heavy
burdens of guilt seemed to evaporate. His spirit seemed
to have power over everything evil.

"Our world is full of evil spirits, but Jesus belonged to
a different world, where the evil was powerless. Best of
all, he opened his world to all who would follow him. We
didn't have to wait until our whole external world was
reformed; then and there he called us into his new world.
Well do I remember that day when I accepted his call. A
new power and peace took hold of me, giving such health
and buoyancy as I had never known. He freed me from all
my fears and guilt. So I left my nets at home, and accompanied Jesus from town to town, watching the joy of those
whom God was blessing. I tell you, Jesus has power to
change a man's world."

"Who are you, that we should listen to you?" asked a
curious bystander.

"My name is Simon Peter, and I am a fisherman from

Capernaum. But I do not speak on my own authority alone; it is Jesus who has sent me."

"What happened to this Jesus?" It was Bar-Joseph who spoke, and Clement surmised from the tone that the elder already knew the answer.

"Our people, to whom Jesus came with the message of life, spurned him. The scribes were enraged by his teaching. The priests were frightened by his prophecies regarding the Temple. The rulers smelled the smoke of revolutionary changes. At the Feast of the Passover they arrested him. The Sanhedrin charged him with lawbreaking, sedition, blasphemy. And the crowd accepted their verdict. As an enemy of both Israel and Rome, he was turned over to Pilate, and Pilate ordered him crucified. That is what happened to God's Servant, the Messiah."

Until now the group had listened silently, with only casual heckling. The message was so novel that at first they did not know quite what to make of it. The conviction of the speaker was so authentic and his presence so fearless that no one dared interrupt his impetuous announcement. But when it seeped into their minds that he was trying to tell them that an unheard-of Galilean who had been killed was none other than their long-expected Messiah, their emotions erupted.

"A strange Saviour this!"

"How could a sinner and a criminal save us?"

"Surely the Sanhedrin was right. How could our people accept such a man as King?"

"What we need is freedom from suffering, not a vain dream like this."

As the weight of these rebuttals piled up, Clement remained silent. After all, he was a stranger here, more interested in getting his bearings than in joining in a street wrangle. The message sounded fanciful, to be sure, but he was not so quick in dismissing it as were some of his neighbors.

Again the voice of the speaker rose above the clamor. He betrayed no surprise or apprehension at the increasing opposition, but began to deal one by one with the more stubborn objections.

"I am not surprised at your reactions, for I myself was slow to believe, and I have heard men in many cities laugh at my story. Of course I had some advantages, for I heard Jesus speak and I saw the marvelous things that he did. I shared in the wave of renewed hope that spread wherever he went. Even with all these signs, I did not at first recognize this man as the Messiah. But I could not escape the fact that here God was actually forgiving and redeeming men. I saw Jesus cast out demons. I was a witness as blind men were enabled to see, deaf men to hear, and the lame to walk. I saw how God's peace and freedom replaced anxiety and slavery. I became convinced that God through this Prophet was actually restoring Israel.

"And then I went up with Jesus to Jerusalem to observe the Passover. I was with him when the soldiers arrested him. This was too much for me as it is for you. My faith gave way. In fear of my life I fled. When Pilate executed him on the cross, my disappointment was bitter. I supposed that this Leader had betrayed us all, trapping us by playing on our emotions. To be sure, he had warned us in advance that the Kingdom could come only through suffering, but it seemed too much to believe that the Messiah himself must suffer. How could a crucified man have power to establish God's Kingdom? Not being able to trust such a Saviour, I escaped the soldiers and went back to my fishing. I supposed that the whole affair was closed.

"But it wasn't. God raised Jesus from the dead. Jesus appeared to me and to other followers. At first we couldn't believe it. But he followed us and wouldn't let us go. He made us see that he had died for us, even though we had forsaken him. He persuaded us that God is in earnest about establishing his Kingdom over the hearts of men. Men are so blinded by the world's ways that they kill God's own Son, thinking that they are doing their duty. But God is willing even to sacrifice his Son in order to demonstrate his power over sin and death. God is now beginning his Kingdom in spite of all opposition.

"So when Jesus appeared to us again he called us to follow him. He forgave us for being cowards and traitors. He warned us again that his disciples too must be ready to die; but he assured us that this is the road to new life. Never have I known such courage and freedom and joy as when I accepted this call of the risen Lord. That is why I am here to invite you into fellowship with him. He is offering you the same promise.

"Let me tell you one of his parables:

'A man planted a vineyard and rented it out to tenants. Then he went to another country for a long while. When the rental period was up he sent a collector to the tenants to receive his share of the harvest. But the tenants beat him and sent him away without the rental. And he sent another collector, and they beat him also and threw him out of the vineyard. Then the owner said, I will send my beloved son; perhaps they will respect him. But when the tenants saw him they said to one another, This is the heir; let us kill him, and the inheritance will be ours. This they did. Now what will the owner of the vineyard do to such tenants? Will he not come and destroy them and give the vineyard to others?'

"The beloved Son of this parable is Jesus. The vineyard belongs to him. It is he whom God has chosen as Judge of the living and the dead. He alone is able to save us from the coming wrath. Repent and join the company of those who await his return. If you refuse, you take on yourselves the sin of those who crucified him. If you repent, you will be forgiven and will receive life in his name. His Spirit will come upon you as a sign that you are citizens in his Kingdom. Again this day God speaks to you as he did in the days of Moses: 'See, I have placed before you this day life and good, death and evil.'

"Come with me to the house of Jonas on the Appian Way. There we will meet other disciples and we shall talk further about this good news."

Simon Peter paused, waiting for a response, but the crowd kept tensely silent. A few were inclined to laugh at his message and to drive him away, but each waited for another to lead the attack. Some were fascinated by the astounding words, but they too were hesitant to speak openly. Hearing no rejoinder, the dark fisherman left the porch and walked away. Clement was bewildered, hardly knowing what to think or do. The service of worship, followed by Peter's speech, had struck like a cyclone, and the fragments had not yet had time to settle in his mind. The coming days would give him chance to ponder. So, making a mental note of the location of the house of which Peter had spoken, he withdrew quietly from the jostling company and walked slowly to Bar-Joseph's home.

A Dialogue

THE noon meal at Bar-Joseph's provided a welcome
interlude. The other guests were in no mood either
for commenting on the service or for discussing the
address of the fisherman. They seemed to take the day's
worship for granted, as part of the week's routine, and
were untroubled by the questions which Peter's speech
had provoked in Clement's mind. In fact, the newcomer
was chagrined to notice that prayers and Scriptures which
had absorbed him so completely had had no apparent
effect on his companions. The table talk moved lightly
from one subject to another, from the current prices for
wine to the prospects of an early winter, from the latest
scandal about the emperor to complaints over the water
supply.

During the meal, Clement found it difficult to take part
in this casual chatter. The thoughts of the morning would

not let him alone, but kept rebounding from one wall of his brain to the other. As soon as he was through eating he excused himself and went to his room to see if the seething ideas might be settled down into some sort of order. He knew that something had happened to him that morning, but he could hardly tell what it was. He had to get his bearings. He could not tell in which direction he was moving, but at least he must find out for himself where he stood.

What things, he asked himself, *am I really sure about?* The first answer that suggested itself was the fact that he could not get away from God. *When I drift away from him, I lose my sense of direction. When I come back I regain it. Many times I have ignored his presence, resented his commands, despised his people, but these have been detours from the main road and have usually led back to it. These excursions have taught me that God is guiding me even when I am least aware of it. I never feel right on these detours.*

Through his mind there echoed the words of the first of the benedictions, one of which his family had for years used to open each day:

> "'Blessed art thou, O Lord, our God, and God of our fathers, God of Abraham, God of Isaac, and God of Jacob; the great, mighty, and revered God, God most high, who art the Creator of Heaven and earth, our Shield and the Shield of our fathers, our confidence from generation to generation; Blessed art thou, O Lord, the Shield of Abraham.'"

Clement recalled the surprise of the morning when he had felt that he recognized his father's presence in the synagogue. *That's another fact I cannot get away from,* he mused. *I belong to Israel; Israel does not belong to me.*

Israel belongs to God; God does not belong to us. When my loyalty to God withers, then I feel estranged from his people. When I think that I can get along without my people, this is a rejection of God. The synagogue's prayers today made me feel at home among strangers. But if I had not made the prayers my own, I should have been even more of an alien than the Gentiles in the gallery. Here is my home, and there is no other. Of this I am certain.

At that moment his host knocked at the door and entered to ask if Clement was comfortable. "I hope you will feel quite at home," Bar-Joseph warmly assured him.

"Entirely at home," was the equally sincere reply. "In fact," he continued, "I was just thinking how amazing it is to find myself so much at home in a strange city among people I didn't know until yesterday."

"Did you enjoy our service this morning?" The question reflected more than a casual interest.

"Yes. The worship reminded me of home. It made me realize that when strangers use the same prayers to the same God they cease to be strangers. I expected to be a bit homesick, alone in this huge city, but so far it hasn't happened."

"I am glad of that. We Jews in Rome are a tormented, restless, frenzied folk, hardly knowing what to do or think. I was afraid our fears might disturb you."

"Some of your guests don't seem to worry much. They don't talk as though they were living next door to a volcano."

"But you must not judge by the surface of their conversation. They are simply trying to cover up their wounds. Their fears would drive them mad if they could not complain about the weather."

"One doesn't need to be long in Rome to understand why people are restless. What is going to happen?" Clement repeated to Bar-Joseph the ditty that Romans were singing about the Jews.

"Oh, we'll manage somehow to weather the rough going! God has some purpose, I suppose, in sending us these storms. We may not know why, but he will use us in some way to advance his design for the world. All we can do is to endure our lot, encourage one another, and wait in faith for his help."

"I hope I don't cause you much bother by being here."

"Not at all. I'm very glad to have you around. Tough times are ahead, but if you don't frighten easily you may even enjoy the excitement." With this rather dubious encouragement, Bar-Joseph withdrew, not wishing to intrude himself into his guest's free afternoon.

Clement's respect for his host was growing. It was easy to see that this man was greatly concerned for the interests of the community. Although baffled and somewhat impoverished by the series of misfortunes, he had forgotten his private security in his efforts to help those who were less secure.

I believe that to Bar-Joseph the fate of his people is more important than his own. He might be prosperous; but if they suffered, his success would be empty. He might fail; but if their destiny were realized, he would not care so much that he had failed.

Suddenly Clement checked himself with a sharp question: *Would this be true of me too? Am I actually more concerned over others' fate than my own? Are the agonies of my people my own agonies? No,* he thought, *if tomorrow I am injured or reviled, I shall be more resentful than if another Jew is attacked. But that simply means that Bar-Joseph is more sincere than I am.*

Clement lay down on his pallet for a nap, but sleep did not come. Clashing thoughts made relaxation impossible.

Again and again his mind came back to the question, "Why must the people whom God has chosen suffer so continually?" He thought of Jeremiah's prophecy: "Your wound is incurable." But why should it be incurable? The history of men like Bar-Joseph seemed full of nothing but wounds. From his lips, day after day, through the long years, came the prayer:

> "'Heal us, O Lord our God, from the pain of our heart; and cause weariness and sighing to leave us.'"

As often as this petition was offered it was frustrated. Why?

He knew how his father would reply to this question. He would say: "We have failed to accept the Law, to follow its requirements. We have contaminated Israel by our contacts with the heathen world."

Take my friendship with Julian, for example. Father has always feared what might come of it. He has expected me to adopt Julian's habits in order to smooth our friendship. He told me once that Julian would kill my conscience and make me a pagan. Is that what has happened to me?

Clement had not relished his father's intolerance, partly because it would mean breaking off his friendship with Julian, partly because he could not fully trust a God who demanded such sacrifice. His father's logic seemed sound; nevertheless Clement inwardly resented it. And his resentment had made him suspicious of such simple reasoning: *Why does not God help those who follow the Law most rigorously? If father's position be true, should we not cut ourselves off completely from the pagan world? And is it not impossible for men to draw such a hard-and-fast line between good men and bad?*

For centuries, men like his father had been struggling to improve themselves and the world, but the world had stubbornly resisted them. For all their efforts, it had not greatly changed. God had promised peace and blessedness to his faithful, but this promise had not come true. His Kingdom had not come. What was wrong? Must God wait until men have set their world right? That may never happen. Or will God by some miracle send his Kingdom in spite of the mountainous evils of the world? But how could that happen? Just how could God replace war by peace, starvation by plenty, antagonism by fellowship?

The picture of the fisherman returned. What was so startling about his story was the claim that this miracle had already happened. Through the work of a carpenter, Jesus, God had begun to move the mountain of the world's evil. But if this were true, it would mean that loyal Jews had been following a phantom dream. They had tried so hard to become righteous that they had shut the door of the Kingdom against all but a handful of saints. Proud of their own superiority, they had rejected as inferior none other than God's Son. According to Peter, the real obstacle to the Kingdom's coming was this effort to become better than others. Jesus brought God's Kingdom near to men who recognize the futility of their efforts to become righteous, who admit the impossibility of saving themselves and their world. The Kingdom comes only when a man humbly accepts the gift of God's mercy, without any claim of goodness on his own part.

According to Peter, then, the worst sinners could become saints, and those whom Israel revered as great saints, like his father and Bar-Joseph, were in reality great sinners. Clement resented this charge. Could the wisest and best Jews be so badly mistaken? In their efforts to obey God's Law, were they only fooling themselves? Were all of them wrong, and only this strange fisherman right?

The burden of proof lay with Peter. The truth of his

message depended upon the truth of the claim about this strange Messiah, Jesus. Was he actually the Messiah? Had he been killed by those he came to save? Had he been raised from the dead? Was God in fact establishing his new age now, through the power of this strange King? If this were true, then Peter's words must be considered seriously. Beyond this point Clement realized that he could not push without further information.

Disturbed and uncertain, Clement became so restless that he decided to take a walk. As he was leaving, his host stopped him for a moment at the door. "Would you like me to show you around the neighborhood?" Clement accepted the offer with thanks, and they set off together, just as the sun was dropping over the crest of the Janiculan hill.

The elder's home was on the eastern slope, near the line that divided the ostentatious villas of Roman nobles from the more ordinary dwellings of the Jewish artisans and tradesmen. They first strolled north among the villas, then climbed the hill to get a view of the sunset, and finally circled back through the streets to the south.

Each quickly found that the other was less interested in sight-seeing than in getting better acquainted. They chuckled together over the contrasts between life on the farm and in the city. Bar-Joseph told Clement some amusing jokes about his father—how on a previous visit he had been fleeced by a certain merchant. . . . Gradually their thoughts gravitated to the events of the morning. What did Clement think of the visitor? Although he was glad for this question, Clement tried to conceal the depth of his interest by replying nonchalantly: "I've never heard such a strange message. Do you always provide this sort of attraction for your Sabbath service?"

"Not every Sabbath. But one can expect almost anything

in such chaotic times. Last year we had several self-appointed prophets who announced the end of the world. They stirred up some excitement for a while, but the end did not come. Our people are not easily deceived; they have endured too much. And such prophets only complicate matters."

"Had you ever seen this fisherman before?"

"Yes, he came to our synagogue several weeks ago. He asked for the privilege of reading the lesson, and our elders let him. Then he spoke of this Messiah, and we asked him to confine his preaching to the porch. He stirred up several of the Gentiles and one or two of our own number, but nothing seems to have happened to them. They were back at worship this morning."

"Why didn't you enter into debate with him this morning?" asked Clement.

"I saw that I could accomplish nothing by argument. He meets every objection by appealing to this Messiah, this man who was crucified by Pilate."

"Do you know anything about Jesus?"

"Only what Peter has told us. It is possible that some of the things that he says about Jesus are true; that this teacher from Galilee was repudiated by our leaders and executed by the Romans. He may have taught this idea of God's Kingdom. He may even have healed the sick and cast out demons. But that proves nothing. Other men have been known to do that. What is incredible is the claim that God would choose such a one to be his Messiah. This is not only unbelievable; it is monstrous blasphemy. When Peter first appeared several weeks ago, I asked him several questions, but none of his answers satisfied me.

"'Is it not blasphemy,' I asked, 'to claim that a mere man has been made God's Son? Surely better credentials than these should be required!' To this he answered: 'Yes, it would be blasphemous if Jesus were not actually God's Chosen One. But if he is the Son, and God has made that certain, then it is blasphemy to deny it.' You see, Clement, how slippery such logic becomes."

"Yes, by that logic anyone could claim to be the Messiah, and get away with it. What was your next question?"

"My second question was equally useless: 'What grain of evidence that the Kingdom has come have we to offset the mountains of evidence that it is still kept in heaven?' 'Faith,' he replied, 'makes the grain of evidence sufficient. The prophets predicted that when the Kingdom should appear, the Holy Spirit would be poured out on men. This Spirit has fallen on us, enabling us to see all the evidence we need. You look for the wrong kind of evidence, and therefore fail to see it. It is God's Spirit that enables us to recognize Jesus as Messiah.' Now that is a weak argument, Clement, and you may be sure that not many of our people will accept it. We have been fooled too often to be so gullible as that.

"Knowing that Peter claimed to be a Jew, I tried another line. 'You recognize,' I said, 'the authority of the Law and the sacredness of our community. Do you not undermine these fundamentals by contending that God would select a sinner like Jesus to save other men? Can a sinner save other sinners?' Here again he evaded my point. He granted that the leaders in Galilee branded Jesus as a sinner according to the Law—'but these are only human judgments,' he said. 'This condemnation of Jesus represents only the false standards of scribes and politicians. By choosing this so-called sinner as Messiah, God made clear that man's judgments were here at fault. He made clear that in his sight, Jesus alone was righteous. He was wholly obedient to God, and everyone else was a rebel.'

"You are old enough, Clement," Bar-Joseph continued,

"to know where such reasoning would lead. It would throw all our standards on a rubbish heap. To claim that Jesus alone was righteous would make this lone teacher an authority superior to our Law. Without the Law to guide us, we would be lost.

"Last of all I tried to puncture Peter's neat little talk about the Messiah. 'Do you think that God delivers men from evil by sending a Messiah so powerless that he could be killed? If he could not save himself, how can he save us?' How do you think he wriggled out of that? He began by admitting the difficulty, saying that he himself had once denied Jesus for that very reason. But God had overcome his lack of faith by revealing this Galilean to him as alive, after his death. God had declared that in spite of Jesus' death he had become Messiah, and in spite of his failure he would return soon to deliver those who trusted in him.

"Now how can you debate with a man like that?" concluded the elder. "No argument will convince him of his folly; and no argument will convince me that such a Messiah could really fulfill Israel's hope. You see how all his answers fall back upon these claims about Jesus and his resurrection. And how can anyone prove them? Either they are true or they are false. A worse deception could not be imagined. But there is no need to get angry. God is greater than men, and his truth is everlasting. In the end, he unmasks all false prophets."

Bar-Joseph felt that he had satisfied Clement. And Clement thought so too. Peter's statements now seemed rather absurd. Clement admired the older man's poise and confidence. Here was a man not easily frightened or angered. Yet his argument, without intending to do so, strengthened Clement's eagerness to hear Peter's rebuttal. For in this Galilean fisherman he had detected similar qualities of genuine devotion. How could a man proclaim so fearlessly

a message so obviously absurd? Was he driven to do so by
considerations which Bar-Joseph had not fully understood?
There was a mystery here. Clement's training inclined him
toward outright rejection; yet over against this inclination
was the desire to understand how two men, both believing
in the same God and the same covenant, could arrive at
such completely opposite convictions. His own inner
wrestling with the problem of loyalty to a hopeless cause
made him responsive to both extremes.

Perhaps during the week, he thought, *I will go to the
house of Jonas and hear how Peter defends his case.*

CHAPTER 6

A Dilemma

SUNDAY daybreak found Clement eager to get on with the work for which Sabinus had brought him to Rome. Hurrying into his work clothes, he ate a hearty breakfast and packed his lunch. Because he had farther to go than the others, he left the house of Bar-Joseph early and walked briskly down the hill to the Tiber and across the bridge. Here he paused to look downstream at the barges anchored at the wharves. Their decks were beginning to bustle with activity, stevedores loading and unloading the cargo that had been brought up from the ocean port at Ostia. Upstream the scene was quieter and more beautiful. Here in the middle of the river lay an island park, carefully landscaped and terraced.

Ahead of him and to the right Clement saw the ruins of the Circus Maximus, where the great fire had started. The rising sun etched the skyline of the Palatine hill, a pattern of towers and walls with which he was becoming familiar: the palaces of Tiberius, Caligula, and Augustus. Leaving the bridge, he took the path that led by the Temple of Castor into the Forum, where in front of the Senate House he turned right, into the Argiletum road. Thus to cut across the nerve center of the vast empire brought a thrill of excitement. Then Clement began to climb up the Esquiline, his curiosity drawn now by the shops which had been gutted by flames, now to buildings undergoing repair, now to a bookstall or a clothing store that had escaped damage.

He arrived at Sabinus' residence just as Julian and a local freedman were mixing the mortar and bringing the tools from the shed. Julian and Clement were responsible for laying the stones; the other worker, Lentulus, was assigned to carry stones and mortar. With the fresh vigor of the morning they swung into their routine—not too fast, for the job was a long one and the foundations had to be laid with care; and not too slow, for they respected Sabinus' importance and his good will too much to disappoint him by loafing. Today they hoped to get the outer walls well started. Their work provided a rhythm of alternation: selecting the stone, chiseling off the rough sides, spreading mortar, laying the stone, more mortar, then the plumb line and level. Their minds were on the work, and their spirits sang with the pleasure of building. Noon came quickly, and they ate lunch sitting under the cypress trees in the garden.

"What did you do yesterday?" asked Clement.

"Lentulus showed me these eastern suburbs and took me out to the camp of the Imperial Guards. We played games with some soldiers and then came home. By the way, some of the soldiers mentioned that they might soon be dispatched to your homeland. They are expecting a riot call from Judea. And what did you do yesterday?"

Clement hesitated. He half wanted to be drawn into a discussion of his personal problems, but he feared to venture into fields which these men could not understand. So in a flat tone he replied: "Nothing special. I attended the Synagogue of the Olive Tree and talked with some of my father's friends."

"Anything stirring among the Jews?" asked Lentulus abruptly, thinking of the rumors of growing unrest.

"Nothing new," answered Clement. "I did hear a strange story." He managed to keep his voice noncommittal. "Have you ever heard of a man from Galilee by the name of Jesus?"

"Never," replied Julian with a flicker of interest, for he knew his friend well enough to know when something special was on his mind.

"Why would we know anything about affairs in Galilee?" Lentulus' answer was a curt gibe.

"Yesterday," continued Clement, ignoring the barb, "a visitor at the synagogue told us a strange tale about this Jesus. About thirty years ago this fellow created a commotion in Galilee. He announced that God had sent him to prepare men for a new age, the days of the Messiah. He called for everyone to repent, and pointed to signs of coming judgment. He even had power to drive out demons and to cure the sick. The common folk took him seriously, but soon he ran afoul of the Law. Our leaders in Jerusalem, with the Roman governor, Pilate, came to fear his influence, so they executed him."

"Nothing peculiar about that," remarked Lentulus. "Your people are always getting worked up by some hothead who yells about the end of the world. If you didn't dream so much about the future, you wouldn't cry so much about the present. When one of your dreamers begins to get out of hand, what else can Rome do but execute him?"

"I know that almost every month a rebel has been executed," replied Clement in a conciliatory tone. "That's what an army is for. But according to the speech of this man Peter, whom I heard yesterday, this case was different. According to Peter, who was there, this Jesus actually was God's Son, sent to save his people—and to save them not so much from Rome as from the whole of this present age. Peter says that he is sure of this. When he was asked how he knew it, he answered that after Jesus was crucified and buried, God raised him from the dead, to continue his work of saving the world. He said that Jesus appeared to him and sent him to proclaim the new age. Anyone who wishes to enter the Kingdom of this Messiah may do so. All he needs to do is to repent and follow Jesus. If he surrenders his stake in this present age, God will give him life in the coming age."

At that, Lentulus' repressed derision exploded. "What a tale! Only a fool would believe it. You Jews remind me of a nest of baby mice in an empire of cats, each of you debating who will be King Mouse and each of you dreaming of a land of cheese." And he stalked off. He was not angry with Clement; he found the episode too amusing for that.

Julian too was amazed that his cautious friend had been interested in such a tale, but out of deference he did not speak of his surprise. "You see, Clement," he remarked, "how this religious interest of you Jews strikes the average Roman. And you must admit that such a story is as weird as any myth in Ovid. We are too realistic, too well educated, to be taken in by a yarn like that. How can anyone believe in a God who might act like that? In fact, when you say 'God' in that sober tone of yours, we haven't the vaguest notion what you're talking about."

This caused Clement to pause. Unexpectedly his friend had deflected the conversation from the story of Jesus to the question of God. Remembering his moments of commitment in the synagogue, he thought to himself: *Has God put me into this situation to test me? Will I deny God before these friends like a coward, in order to keep their respect? Must I apologize for my faith? Do I fear them more than I fear God?* To ask the question thus gave him no alternative but to say something.

He began his rejoinder in a subdued tone. He did not want to seem to wear a chip on his shoulder; nor did he want to antagonize Julian. "Yes, what you say is true. It is hard for a Gentile to know what we are talking about when we say 'God.' To Gentiles it is quite unnecessary to speak of God, except as some vague idea of a philosopher or some crude superstition. It is different with us. To us, God is not an idea, which we can pick up or cast off, for he is the only real Power. He created all men and he is their Judge. As King, he alone has the right to rule our lives. As Lord, his purpose alone will be fulfilled. Apart from him, life has neither starting point nor goal. Every Jew is trained in this faith from his earliest years."

Julian had no desire to doubt his friend's sincerity or to ridicule his simple faith. But Clement's very earnestness demanded some reply. "But why take God so seriously? If he exists, we can't know him. And if we did, what difference would it make? You should read Seneca. I've just been looking over his recently published letters to Lucilius. In one of them he says this: There are three possibilities: Either fate has determined everything in advance and gives no free play to our plans, in which case we are caught in a chain that drags us along in its clutches; or,

God as Arbiter of the universe has arranged everything, in which case all that remains for us is to obey him cheerfully; or, chance governs everything, driving and tossing human affairs about in a haphazard fashion, and we must simply endure being played with by the whims of accident. In any case, whether human affairs are in the hands of fate, Providence, or chance, our only sensible reaction is to follow our reason as far as it will help us."

"How far does reason help us in a world as baffling as ours? If reason can't tell us what power governs our lives, how can we trust it?" Clement enjoyed his infrequent opportunities for putting Julian on the defensive in such an argument.

Julian accepted the challenge with vigor and began summoning up the teachings which his father, an ardent follower of Seneca, had impressed on his memory. "If there is a God," he began, "then he has given each of us a mind to use. By using our reason, we can distinguish between what lies within our power and what lies outside our power to change. Our desires, for example, do lie within the range of control. We can so limit our hopes that they will not deceive us. Cease to hope for the impossible and we cease to fear. The mind that frets over the future is a mind vulnerable to every turn of fate. Live in the present only and you will never be wretched. Now isn't that good common sense?"

"It's quite true," replied Clement, "that hopes produce fears. My hopes make me restless, and perhaps by abandoning them I could become happy. But wouldn't that be an empty sort of happiness? No doubt a sparrow is happy, but can a man be much of a man without dreams of a better tomorrow?"

"If he wants happiness, he must sacrifice his dreams,"

replied Julian. "Seneca insists that the only truly poor man is one who craves something more than he has. The only rich man is the one who is perfectly content with what he has. The poor man fears future losses. The rich man is ready for death at any moment; so, whatever happens, his mind remains unworried and tranquil."

"Seneca's god makes him satisfied; our God makes us perpetually dissatisfied," admitted Clement. "Our God makes promises of future reward to each of us and to our people as a whole. Those of us who can't forget those promises are the ones who suffer most. You say that we can be happy only by giving up our hopes. The Law and the Prophets tell us that we shall be happy only when God fulfills his promises."

Their conversation had succeeded at least in showing how far apart they were. Was any compromise possible? Each knew that the other had already made up his mind and that it would be impossible by argument to come to an agreement. Their friendship made the breach more painful, and neither wanted to widen the breach. They were therefore secretly relieved to hear Lentulus call them back to work. And, since this was the sort of discussion that needed concentration, they tacitly agreed to let the matter drop until an opportunity should return.

Later Julian began: "I wish we could get Bar-Joseph and Seneca together to hear them debate. Both of them seem to say the same things, yet the words mean something quite different. For example, both say that man's happiness comes from obeying God's laws. For Seneca, this means that to be happy we should be as rational and natural as possible. If we wish to avoid excessive pain, it is rational to accept whatever happens as the will of God. Reason teaches us to rely only upon ourselves. To each man it is enough if he faces each day with courage, if he is faithful to his friends, if he avoids intemperance and injustice, and if he makes the best use of each situation."

"Bar-Joseph would certainly agree with the Stoic ideals of temperance, justice, courage, and faithfulness," replied Clement, eager to make the most of the common ground. "But he would argue that we can't attain those ideals by relying on ourselves. God has some purpose for our lives, other than simply to make us contented. And he has some purpose for all of us together, Gentiles as well as Jews— some reason for making us unhappy over present conditions. If God be actually the Ruler of our lives, can we ever be happy until his Kingdom is actually established? Surely he doesn't intend to inflict world-wide suffering just in order that a few men like Seneca can learn to resign themselves to fate!"

"Seneca is a good example," admitted his friend. "He believes that every man must be absolutely just. Yet he has been treated with rank injustice. Nero, you know, was one of his students. But now the emperor will have nothing to do with him and has exiled him from Rome. Rumor has it that Seneca's life will be forfeited as soon as Nero finds the right opportunity to strike. But Seneca shows that he is superior to Nero by being ready to commit suicide should the need arise. Seneca does not fear death; Nero does. Seneca remains just by being willing to suffer injustice from others."

"You are a great admirer of Seneca, aren't you?" asked Clement.

"My father thinks that he is the greatest living Roman. And the more I read of his writings, the more I think so too."

"Then let us grant that Seneca is a hero, and Nero a beast. Now isn't there some flaw in a universe that permits

the beasts to destroy the heroes? Can we trust nature if
nature's law seems to give the tyrant power over the wise
man?"

"But Seneca's happiness lies beyond Nero's power to
destroy, so long as he remains devoted to a life of virtue.
Nero destroys his own happiness, not Seneca's. Isn't that
perhaps the secret of life: the world is a good world because in it a man like Seneca can achieve happiness?"

"Sounds like a cruel world to me. Aren't you admitting
that God is unjust to the just men in order to give them a
chance at happiness?"

"But, Clement, what is the alternative?"

"The Law and the Prophets assure us that God has
promised to his loyal subjects a place in his Kingdom. No
matter how terribly the good man suffers for his loyalty,
God will make some good come out of his suffering. God's
justice is as certain as the mountains."

"How long have good men suffered?" probed Julian.

"For many generations."

"Then if your God is just, he surely has delayed his reward. How long must a good man wait for his happiness?"

"That's just the question that bothers me," admitted
Clement. "As a Jew, I cannot admit that the Creator can
be either cruel or weak. Yet actually the cruel men seem to
be most powerful."

"I should think you would be slow to attack Seneca's
god, then," replied Julian, quickly taking advantage of
Clement's admission. "At least, Seneca can defend the
claim that the god of reason has provided man with power
to be both just and happy. Your view, by comparison, con-
tradicts itself. Either your God is just, but lacks the power
to defeat evil, or he is powerful enough to guide the for-
tunes of men, but lacks justice."

"You seem to have me trapped. I confess I don't know

the way out," Clement said slowly. "In either case, however, whether we choose to follow Seneca or Moses, our lot is not an easy one. The man who seeks justice is bruised and battered by injustice."

Having again arrived at a problem which did not yield to discussion, the two comrades returned to stones and mortar. Julian, it seemed, could pick up and lay down his thoughts at will, like the blocks with which he was building. His thoughts did not engage the deepest layer of interest, but served rather to occupy idle moments. Clement, on the other hand, found it harder, when he was mentally encased in a corridor with closed doors, not to continue trying one knob after another. But now the doors remained locked, and none could be made to yield.

"Strange," he muttered to himself. "Julian has forced me into the same dilemma as yesterday's service did. However tough the problem is, neither Jew nor Gentile can escape it."

CHAPTER 7

An Arrest

CLEMENT now decided that it was quite useless to fret over his problems longer. Perhaps Bar-Joseph had the right answer, or Seneca, or Peter. Probably no one had it. In any case he could not be expected to solve a problem which had tormented men for centuries. And however men were intended to find happiness, he himself was not becoming any happier by constantly battering his head against closed doors. Julian seemed to be right; he did take himself too seriously. *Who am I*, he thought, *to be trying to solve such problems?*

Monday passed very happily for the three workers. They whistled and sang as the sun and their work warmed their spirits. Clement joined wholeheartedly and even gaily in the songs and banter. He seemed, indeed, like a different person. Freedom from his earlier preoccupation made him a pleasant companion. Lentulus and Julian were

75

eager to avoid the friction which their earlier discussion
had produced. In the case of Lentulus, there was a definite discomfort in venturing into strange fields of thought.
He was not at home in matters of religious belief, and he
usually tried to cover up his ignorance by bluster and
ridicule whenever such questions were opened. Julian's
attitude seemed to be: "Let everyone believe whatever
he wishes. But why worry over questions that can't be answered?" Clement had decided that when all doors are
locked against one, it is the part of wisdom to make the
most of living in the firmly closed corridor. At times he
felt the urge to try the knobs again, but he checked himself with a resigned, "What's the use?" or, "Don't be a
fanatic!"

On Tuesday it was Lentulus who made Clement realize
that he was still shut in the corridor of closed doors.
Lentulus had stumbled on a strange coincidence. "The
other day," he began, at the first pause in the stonelaying,
"you mentioned one of your Jewish patriots, an agitator
called Jesus. Last night I was attending the shows at Nero's
Circus with some soldier friends. I found that two of them
had been on duty in Judea. I told them your yarn and
asked if either had ever heard of this Galilean. My question set one of them thinking. He is an officer, an older
man who has been everywhere. He told me that his first
term of military service, long ago, had been as an ordinary soldier under Pilate's command. One of his first assignments in Judea was to help execute several Jewish
criminals. One of them was this man Jesus from Nazareth.
I asked him why he should remember this man and not the
others."

"'I suppose,' he replied, "it was due to the fact that
this was the first time I was commanded to torture civil-

ians. It's a bit different, you know, from striking down an enemy in battle.'

"He seemed to be recalling something else, and I asked whether he knew anything more about Jesus.

" 'Yes,' he replied, 'there was something curious about him. He seemed so harmless. He was quiet and gentle, treating us as if we were his friends. Most victims, of course, start screaming and swearing in rage and hatred. This one accepted death so naturally that we were all amazed.' "

Clement was caught off balance by Lentulus' story. He did not want to be put in the position of defending Jesus. That would give Lentulus an opening for his biting satire. On the other hand, to ridicule Jesus in order to please Lentulus would be cowardly. So he contented himself with remarking, "That soldier must have a good memory"; and then, with a thrust at Lentulus, "He, at least, concedes that there might be a good Jew." Secretly he wondered what Peter would have said to this soldier who had helped to crucify the man from Nazareth.

After Lentulus had finished his report, Julian added an item of news.

"Yesterday evening," he ventured, "I asked Sabinus whether he knew anything about Jesus. He is in such close touch with the police that I knew he might have recent information. He recalled that, when Claudius was emperor, disciples of this man caused a flare-up among the Roman Jews. In order to preserve the peace, a number of them were expelled from the city. That seemed to solve the problem for a time, but in a few years the Christians filtered in again. This time they were allowed to stay. They hold a few meetings here and there without objection from the police, who have not yet been instructed whether to treat their gatherings as legal assemblies of Jews or as an illegal religion. There have been some disturbances, and on several occasions the police have thrown them into jail; but in the main they have been peaceable enough. Sabinus recalled that about two years ago several of their more fanatical leaders were executed. The most prominent was a traveling tentmaker from Syria by the name of Paul. The police beheaded him. Since the great fire, however, the police have been too busy to bother them much."

"It is strange," remarked Lentulus, "how hard it is to exterminate such crazy cults. Rome seems to be a hothouse where they flourish. Everywhere one stumbles over groups who hold the most fanatic superstitions. In comparison with them, your synagogues, Clement, are almost as respectable as the Temple of Jupiter."

Clement could see that the conversation was threatening to destroy the good will which had been developing among them. But Lentulus' last sentence had been designed as a friendly gesture. He seemed almost ready to include Clement with the decent Romans, as over against the foreign faddists. Clement, for his part, was desperately eager to accept this gesture, so he tried to direct the conversation away from controversy into safer areas.

"How do the police determine which religions are innocent and which are dangerous?"

"I don't think they follow any set rule," Lentulus replied. "Of course most of the religions are registered with the Government and are recognized as legal. The others are always under suspicion, especially new ones. If they disturb the peace or antagonize the authorities or agitate against Roman customs, then they are suppressed."

"Had you noticed how many police there are patrolling the streets?" Julian observed. "Are they afraid of something?"

"Yes," Lentulus assured them. "It's like the time when the latest attempt was made to assassinate Nero."

"Tell us about it," urged Clement, glad to be on a subject both safe and interesting. The day passed quickly now, with both Clement and Julian drawing from their comrade his recollections of exciting times in Rome. It was an absorbing story.

* * *

On his way home that evening Clement was piecing together again the chain of stories which he had heard from Lentulus. Some he would file away in his mind to tell his father; some would provide conversation for the evening meal.

As he was crossing leisurely through the Forum, he noticed at one of the entrances a crowd being harangued by a speaker. Curious, he drew near. Suddenly, with a start of dread, he recognized the speaker. *Can't I escape the fellow?* he thought, for it was Peter. Clement's first impulse was to avoid the group, but curiosity proved too strong.

As he slipped within earshot, he heard the voice boldly accusing the listeners. Referring to the ruins of the city, he told them that the fire had been no accident, but a divine warning. Soon a greater catastrophe would befall Rome, and indeed the whole world. In such happenings God punishes his children for their sins and gives them a chance to repent before the really terrible fire comes, the fire of Final Judgment.

At this the Jews among the listeners stirred apprehensively. Fear of anti-Semitic outbursts had made it an unwritten law for them not to discuss the fire in the presence of Gentiles. And this immigrant Jew was not only discussing it; he was using it as threat:

"God spoke through his Prophet Jesus, saying:

" 'As it was in the days of Noah,
　They ate, they drank, they married, they were given in
　　marriage,
　Until the day that Noah entered the ark,
　And the flood came and destroyed them all. . . .
　So shall it be also in the days of the Son of man.

" 'As it was in the days of Lot—
　They ate, they drank, they bought, they sold, they
　　planted, they builded,
　But in the day when Lot went out of Sodom
　It rained fire and brimstone from heaven and destroyed
　　them all—
　So shall it be also in the days of the Son of man.' "

It would have been hard to imagine a message more likely to stir up the antagonism of the Romans, struggling as they were to rebuild their city. One of them shouted back: "You Jews are haters of the human race. All of you ought to be driven from the city."

To this, one of the Jews gave a quick reply: "Don't take this madman seriously. I too am a Jew, and I ask you to believe that we Jews in Rome are not responsible for this crazy doctrine. This man does not speak for us. We are loyal citizens. We too lost our homes. We are as eager as any of you to rebuild a more beautiful city."

Then Peter gave his answer to the heckler. "I don't hate your city," he said, "and I do not hate you. Why should I risk arrest from your police to bring you this message? The question for you to answer is, Why do you hate God? Why do you keep turning away from the only God who can save you from that final fire?"

Another heckler broke in loudly: "We do not hate the gods. We have worshiped them regularly for centuries. We have made sacrifices to them to appease their anger in burning our city. Our only sin is that we have allowed so many vermin like you to live here. It is you who have blasphemed our gods, ignored our temples, refused to honor our emperor, and you have drawn down this penalty upon us. Why should you be allowed to live in a city that is sacred to our gods? Why should we tolerate you who hate us and our gods?"

"It is true," replied Peter calmly, "that you have your gods and that you have worshiped them loyally for many years. It is true that we Jews cannot worship them without being traitors to our God. Our very presence in your city creates trouble for you; for the God whom we worship declares through us that your gods are idols which deceive you. You have power to kill us and to drive us out. But you do not have power to silence the God of heaven and earth. Kill us, and you would still have to answer to him. He would send others to raise the question which you dare not face: Are your gods false idols? I do not speak on my own authority. The one true God has sent me to call you away from your dead idols to seek the living God. Blessed is he. I could not stand here apart from his power. He has declared war on all the forces of evil and he will win that war."

The rumble of hostility grew louder, and Simon Peter had to raise his voice. "Let me tell you how I know this to be true. Let me tell you of the Messiah through whom God will accomplish these things. God has sent his Son, Jesus of Nazareth. . . ." But the roar of the angry mob drowned out his voice. And at that moment there came into the Forum an armed squad, led by Tigellinus himself, chief of the secret police. The crowd vanished, and Peter was left alone. As Clement watched, two of the police took Peter's arms and, unresisting, he was led away. In fact, he seemed not to be frightened, but began talking to his captors. More stunned than Peter, Clement found himself walking toward Bar-Joseph's home. *So that is what happens, after all,* he mused, *when a man speaks for God in this world of hatred. Should I too have proclaimed my faith in God?*

No, was the answer, *this is none of my business. I am only a stranger here, and a lone individual is helpless in a huge city. Peter must have known that the police wouldn't let him get away with such a message. Perhaps he wanted to be arrested. At least, even if I were on his side, what good would it have done for me to be arrested with him?*

This answer satisfied Clement, and yet he could not forget the incident. And every recollection of it became a pin, pricking his sensitive body. The more he tried to forget, the less he was able to escape the irritation. *I tremble at the sight of the police; Peter seems to be fearless. What is it that makes him take such risks? Why does this message appear so urgent to him? And why should a powerful empire be so afraid of a roving fisherman? Is he actually a prophet, or simply a dangerous fanatic?*

Back again in the corridor of closed doors, he thought, *and pushed there against my will.* Clement didn't like it. A peevish mood caught him. *Why can't I get away from all these questions? Why all these coincidences that keep me from being myself, an ordinary worker in Rome?*

He could not bring himself to mention the incident of Peter's arrest at the supper table. Bar-Joseph's guests were already too worried to be further disturbed, and his own spirit was too divided to permit speech. After the evening meal he asked his host for stationery and began a letter, long overdue, to his father. Under these circumstances the task became a difficult one, and he ended by saying little of what had been on his mind.

*   *   *

CLEMENT TO HIS FATHER, MATTATHIAS, GREETING:

I rejoice to be able to report that our journey to Rome was carried out according to plan. Mother's lunch was tasty and ample, and Bar-Joseph has made me very welcome. The work on Sabinus' house is starting well. He says it will keep Julian and me busy at least until spring. The wages will easily cover my board and lodging and other expenses.

On the Sabbath I worshiped at the Synagogue of the Olive Tree and I met your friends, Jason and Ezra. There was some excitement over a preacher from Judea who announced that the Messiah has come and that the days of Israel's captivity are nearly over. A dangerous message, as this preacher found out when he was arrested this evening! Conditions are both unstable and exciting. Our people are likely to have difficulty at any time, especially if such prophets get too numerous. But my faith is steady, and I am confident for the future, however dark it may be. [*Am I really*, thought Clement as he wrote, *or am I saying this just to keep up my courage?*] I am finding out how difficult it is for Israel to serve God as a despised minority in a pagan city. How long will God allow his servants to suffer this captivity? What do you think about the hope of a Messiah? Are these disturbances, perhaps, signs of the last days?

So many things have happened that it seems much more than a week since I left home. Sabinus salutes you and says that you have trained me well in laying a foundation. Bar-Joseph greets you and asks that you send some cabbage and winter squash when they are harvested. Send plenty, for this is a large family.

May God give you peace.

PART TWO · TRANSITION

CHAPTER 8

On the Appian Way

ON THE following evening, when Clement left work, he took a new route. Circling around the Palatine hill, he located the Appian Way and began walking slowly toward the suburbs. To him this was a new section of the city, and the landmarks held great interest. But his mind was on his destination—the house of Jonas, where the Christians met every evening for worship. He was not sure why he was going or what he would do when he got there. Perhaps he would be unable to find it; perhaps if he found it he would not have the nerve to enter.

He was still very curious about what had happened to Peter. Julian and Lentulus had heard nothing of the arrest, so there was no one from whom he could get a report unless from the Christian disciples at Jonas' home. But more than curiosity was responsible for this trip. Perhaps it was a fascination similar to that of a fire. One is attracted to it just because it is dangerous and unpredictable. At any moment the flames may spread, leaping over obstacles to nibble at a new building. At any moment one may have to move to get out of their path. Or with a lull in the wind, the flames may die down a bit before a new spurt of destruction begins. Evidence of police opposition against the Christians was for Clement an invitation to get as close as possible to the danger zone without getting burned. And there was surely no law against a visit to another man's home.

Yet Clement was aware that more even than the lure of the dangerous was tugging at him. Perhaps it was the attraction that fearless people exert over the timid. Those who are afraid of a snake may be quite hypnotized by the fearless poise of the snake charmer. They want to borrow some of his courage, or at least to imagine themselves as free of dread as he is. Still on the walls of Clement's memory was the picture of Peter's accepting arrest—unafraid and quiet. In Peter's confidence Clement had detected something of the strength of a granite block. And he wondered if the other Christians were equally courageous and calm.

Perhaps other emotions were urging Clement on this secret quest. Was he, after all, guilty of choosing an easy course, compromising his faith to suit his friends and hiding his convictions to avoid embarrassment? Or did he suspect that Peter's message really did hold a key to the doors that had shut him in? Whatever the conflicting reasons, he was not too eager to find Jonas' house. Had his search been unsuccessful, his mind would have been relieved. In fact, at one street corner he paused, inclined to turn back. But the pull forward was stronger than the desire to go back. Clement had a persistent, if not a bullheaded disposition. He did not easily cancel a projected venture.

After walking a mile or more from the Palatine hill he came to a section of tenements obviously inhabited by his own people. Near the center of the district he observed several people walking down an alley to a four-story building. A meeting seemed to be in progress, so he inquired of one of the group if this was the house of Jonas. They not only answered him but invited him to go with them. This was more than he had counted on, for now he could hardly avoid accepting the invitation.

Whatever fears he may have had, however, were quickly put aside. Jonas welcomed him cordially with the salutation: "May peace be yours, brother."

"May peace rest upon this house," replied Clement. The two adjoining rooms of Jonas' apartment were crowded. Some thirty people had gathered, subdued and expectant, in spite of the congestion. Toward Clement, as he slipped into a corner seat, only a few glances were directed. In them Clement detected a trace of fear.

They are more afraid of me than I of them, he thought. *They know that I may be here as an informer, to get evidence for the police.*

The first glances of his neighbors, however, seemed to satisfy them. His serious Jewish face assured the fearful that he was not an enemy. He was grateful that they should accept him so readily and should allow him to remain anonymous and inconspicuous in his corner.

Without announcement the group quieted down in prayer, the silence broken occasionally by a fervent "Father" or a confident "Amen." One disciple prayed for Peter and the brothers who were in prison. Another gave a petition for the police and the rulers, that God might forgive their blindness and draw them to follow the Messiah. Another asked that their witness to the Lord might be effective in reaching new converts.

Presently a speaker arose, and the congregation fixed its attention on him.

"Welcome, men of Rome," he began. "Some of you are inquirers who wish to hear more about our Messiah. Some of you are his disciples, eager to give your witness to him. May each of you hear the voice of God, so that you may be delivered from this age of death to the age of life.

"Our brother Peter was arrested last night. He was proclaiming the good news in the Forum when a squad of policemen broke up the meeting. Today I was able to see him and take him some food. He doesn't know what charges will be made against him or how long he may be held. But he sent word that we should be of good courage, continuing our task as if nothing had happened. He is grateful for this opportunity to show his love for the Lord, and wants us to rejoice that no suffering is able to stifle our hope."

This was the information that Clement had wanted. Yet, far from satisfying his curiosity, it whetted his thirst for more. *How can a prisoner who may be killed ask his friends so lightly to rejoice over his fate?*

"This is not the first time Peter has been in jail," the speaker was saying now. "In Jerusalem and in other cities he has given his testimony as a prisoner. Other brothers are also in jail, and some of our number have been killed here in Rome. You will remember that only two years ago the Apostle Paul gave his life in the preaching of God's message. You will remember, too, how he taught us to look upon such a fate.

"To suffer for the good news is a mark of our salvation. For we suffer because we preach the story of the cross. And this story is folly to those who perish with the world,

but it is the power of God to those who are called into the
new world. It causes some to be offended, but others are
persuaded by it to believe. And this is the way that God
separates those who are blinded by earthly wisdom from
those who are able to see the road to life.

"Peter's arrest is thus the way by which our enemies reveal their trust in the world's power. And it is the way we
reveal our trust in God. Men may be able to arrest us; but
they cannot arrest God's power or keep him from fulfilling
his promise to give us the Kingdom."

With the other inquirers, Clement was intrigued by the
audacity of these ideas. It seemed so obvious that enemies
held the whip hand over this group. What could this weak
and paltry number do against the power of Rome? Yet they
seemed to treat every evidence of their insignificance as
a sign of their strength. They seemed to believe that God
had given them everything, in a world where they could
call nothing their own. He recalled that this was precisely
the flavor of Peter's speeches, a mood of calm defiance of
the world and inner indifference to what others might do.
Watching closely the disciples sitting near him, he noticed
a serene joy on their faces, as if the new disaster had
simply increased their peace and security. Were they
crazy or had they actually found some power which enabled them to welcome danger as an opportunity and
defeat as a victory?

"I don't understand what you're talking about," interrupted a man sitting next to Clement, and almost putting
into words Clement's own questions. "What sort of power
is it that can stand against the power of Rome? God has
promised his people deliverance, not death. You seem to
feel that death is actually a mark of deliverance."

"Yes, it is," was the candid reply. "Our Messiah was
killed, and by his death he delivered us from the fear of

death. Let me tell you the story from the beginning. The beginning, of course, goes back to the earliest prophets who brought God's word to a rebellious people. The people have always rejected the prophets that were sent to them. Yet a few people have always accepted their witness to God. I can't tell you that whole story. Read the Law and the Prophets.

"But God will not let his people go. He sends prophet after prophet to offer the key to life. In our days, he began again his effort to save us by sending John the Baptizer. As in the days of Isaiah, John came as a voice that shouted:

> "'Prepare in the wilderness a road for the Lord,
> Make level in the desert a highway for our God.
> Every valley will be raised,
> Every hill will be lowered,
> Uneven places will be leveled,
> Crooked places will be straightened;
> The glory of the Lord will be revealed,
> And all men everywhere will see it:
> For God himself has declared this.'"

"But what did John actually accomplish?" asked Clement's neighbor.

"He accomplished the mission for which God had sent him. He appeared from the wilderness, like Elijah, and aroused the people by his call to repentance. Like Elijah, he wore a camel's skin and lived on locusts and wild honey. This is what he shouted to the people of Judea:

> "'You children of snakes! Who has warned you to flee from the wrath which is coming? If you really want to repent, produce fruit to show it. Even now God has laid the ax against the root of the trees; the tree that does not yield the fruit of repentance will be cut down and burned. Do not start saying to yourselves, We are safe, for Abraham is our father. I warn you that God can turn these stones into sons of Abraham.'

"As in the days of the earlier prophets, men had been longing for the day of deliverance from the cruel injustices of life. But most men, even the Jews who knew God's promises, had become skeptical, saying, 'It can't happen to us.' But a few had patiently waited in expectation of deliverance, saying, 'It can happen here.' Now John appeared with the word: 'It will happen here, and very soon. Get ready now.'"

"But you still haven't told us what he accomplished," came back the heckler insistently.

"Well, in his day it seemed that he didn't accomplish much," the speaker admitted. "He met the same fate as Peter. He stirred up a hornet's nest by attacking Herod, and the king threw him into jail and later beheaded him. But not until after John had fulfilled his mission. For there were a few who did accept his warning as God's truth. Peter was one of them, and Jesus himself, our Messiah, came and was baptized by John, entering the road of repentance. When John's mouth was closed, it did not mean that God stopped speaking. Jesus took up the cry and carried the good news to Galilee.

"John's message was the turning point, for, with Jesus' preaching, God's Kingdom actually began to arrive among men. The Law and the Prophets had been God's way of saving men until John's work was done. Since then, the Kingdom of God has itself begun to scatter its power. Jesus came with the news: 'It has happened here. The Holy Spirit has already begun to draw men into the circle of the new age.'"

"Do you mean that the Kingdom of God actually appeared in the work of this man, and that the door to it is open to men, without waiting for a change in the balance of political power?"

"Yes, that is what God offers us in his Messiah. We can

enter now into the blessedness of the coming age. This is the way Jesus fulfills the message which God has given to the prophets. Jesus began his ministry in Galilee with this proclamation:

> " 'God's Spirit is upon me.
>> He appointed me to preach good news to the poor.
>> He sent me to proclaim release to the prisoners,
>>> to announce the recovery of sight to the blind,
>>> to free those who are enslaved,
>>> to proclaim that God has chosen to begin
>>> the year of salvation.' "

Here, at last, said Clement to himself, *I may find out something definite about this man whom they call the Messiah. Perhaps the speaker will give us proof. So far I have only the opinions of these people.*

"I must make this clear," the speaker was trying to meet the skepticism in the back row. "Jesus cannot introduce into his Kingdom men who will not believe him. He cannot free captives or heal blind men who insist on doubting his authority. The Kingdom comes near only to those who are ready to receive it. That was proved over and over while he was teaching in Galilee.

"One Sabbath he was preaching in the synagogue at Capernaum. Four men came, carrying on a bed a man who was paralyzed. When Jesus saw their faith, he announced to the paralytic, 'Son, your sins are forgiven.' But the scribes who were there protested: 'How can you say things like that? Who except God can forgive sins? This is blasphemy!' But Jesus answered their protest: 'What are you objecting to? Is it easier to say to this lame man, "Your sins are forgiven," or to say, "Get up, carry your bed, walk"? You see, the Son of man has authority both to forgive sins and to say, "Get up and go home." ' And the sick man got up, picked up his pallet and walked out. Amazed and excited, the people were compelled to praise God and to admit, 'We've never seen anything like this.'

"When he left the synagogue he called a tax collector, Levi, to be a disciple, and Levi followed him. Again the scribes protested: 'Do you mingle like this with tax collectors and sinners?' When Jesus heard he answered: 'It is not the healthy who need a doctor, but the sick. I came to call sinners, not the righteous!'

"Then Jesus met a man who was possessed by an evil spirit. The demon screamed out at Jesus: 'What do you want with us, Jesus of Nazareth? I know who you are, you're the Holy One of God. And you have come here to destroy us.' Then Jesus sharply commanded the demon, 'Be still, and leave this man!' Then the evil spirit made the man retch; but during the convulsion, the demon departed. The men of the synagogue were astounded. 'What does this mean?' they asked. 'What new teaching! What marvelous power!'

"From these stories you will observe that always Jesus was met by both belief and scorn. Men who were eager to accept God's Kingdom as a gift were made whole. Those who could not bring themselves to the point of accepting God's gift would not accept the evidence of sick men made well and crazed men made sane. Even John, who had prepared the way for the Messiah, could not believe that the new day was dawning in such a fashion. From his prison he sent followers to investigate these things that were happening. Jesus told them:

> " 'Go and tell John what you have seen and heard:
>   the blind receive their sight,
>   the lame walk,
>   lepers are cleansed,
>   the deaf hear,
>   the dead are raised up,
>   the poor have the good news.
> Blessed is he who takes no offense at me!'

"Nor was John the only one who found occasion to doubt. The scribes and Pharisees constantly challenged him to show his credentials. On one occasion they cornered him in the Temple and asked, 'By what authority do you do these things?' This was Jesus' answer:

"'Let me ask you a question; answer me, and I will tell you by what authority I do these things. Was the baptism of John from heaven or from men? Answer me.'

And they argued with one another: 'If we say, "From heaven," he will say, "Why then did you not believe him?" But if we say, "From man," we shall lose face before these people, for they believe John was a real prophet. So they answered Jesus, 'We do not know.' And Jesus said to them, 'Then I will not tell you by what authority I do these things.'

"As a matter of fact, the Pharisees were determined not to believe that God could send his Kingdom through such a Messiah. On one occasion Jesus drove a demon of dumbness out of a man. The scribes jeered: 'It is through the devil's own power that you can order these spirits.' But he replied: 'Every kingdom divided against itself is laid waste. And if Satan also is divided against himself, how will his kingdom stand? If it is by the finger of God that I cast out demons, then the kingdom of God has come near to you.'"

Clement was not satisfied with this logic. What connection could there be between the healing of one dumb man and the coming of the Kingdom of God? Certainly not an obvious one. The whole world needed to be cured, and its sickness was more than dumbness. Must not the Messiah free men from such scourges as exile, war, hunger, and tyranny?

"Isn't it a long distance from Galilee to Rome?" he began, feeling his way. "And isn't it a long distance from cur-ing a dumb man to conquering famine and war? Didn't the prophets promise that in God's Kingdom the whole world would be delivered from its agony?"

"God will be faithful to that promise," replied the preacher after a moment's pause. "But how do we know he will be faithful unless he gives us power now that is adequate to meet today's need? If the kingdom of evil is defeated in a dumb man, does not that man know that God's power is able to drive Satan out of the whole creation?"

"The dumb man may think so, but how are we to know? Aren't there other signs more convincing for us, who see everywhere the power of evil?" said Clement's neighbor following his lead.

"It is natural, I suppose," rejoined the speaker, "for us all to be impressed by spectacular signs and to be unimpressed by ordinary events. We suppose that God will save us suddenly by transporting us into a world where no evil exists. And until he works some miracle of that sort we remain faithless and hopeless. In Jesus' day the Pharisees were always annoying him, trying to get some spectacular evidence of the Kingdom's appearance, such as the sun falling from heaven or the moon dripping blood. Once he rebuked them by saying:

" 'The kingdom does not come by waiting until you observe some tremendous miracle when you can say, "Look, here is what we expected!" No, suddenly, where you least expect it, the kingdom will be found all around you—as soon as you can detect what God is doing in your midst. Wherever God drives out Satan from his control over men's lives, there the kingdom appears.'

"But the trouble lies in men's blindness. They cannot see that this deliverance from evil is exactly what the prophets hoped to see. It has happened here, but blind

men continue to say, 'It can't happen here.' Once Jesus
said to the skeptics of his day:

> "'When you see a cloud rising in the west, you say
>   at once, A shower is coming;
>   and so it happens.
> When you see the south wind blowing, you say,
>   It will be terribly hot;
>   and so it happens.
> How blind you are!
>   You are able to forecast the weather;
>   but you are unable to understand
>   what is happening all about you.'"

Addressing the men in the back row, the speaker then
made a direct appeal: "To all of you who do not yet believe in the Messiah, we disciples give our testimony. As
disciples, we know that our Master Jesus is now establishing his Kingdom, because he has delivered us from fear
and futility. Peter in prison and we who worship here are
signs to the world that God has healed us and given us
power. In us he has fulfilled the promise given to Isaiah:

> "'He gives power to the faint;
> He gives strength to the weak.
>   Even the youths shall faint and be weary,
>   the young men shall utterly fall:
>   But they that wait on the Lord shall renew their
>   strength;
>   they shall mount up with wings as eagles;
>   they shall run, and not be weary;
>   they shall walk, and not faint.'

"This power has come to us because Jesus has called us
into his service. We do not preach ourselves, but him. He
was a man like us, born in the lineage of David, a carpenter who worked in his Nazareth shop until God called him
into the path of preaching the good news. He trusted

wholly in God's goodness and obeyed his call with complete faithfulness. He was severely tempted, as we are
tempted, to doubt God's power, and to rely on men's ability to find security and peace. But he resisted every temptation. He followed God's guidance in proclaiming the
news of the Kingdom. He loved all men, especially the sick,
the despised, the poor, the sinners. His word brought
power and hope to them. And he taught them how those
who seek the Kingdom must live before God—in perfect
obedience, humility, sincerity, trust, gentleness, self-forgetfulness, and love. He himself was the perfect example
of the faithfulness that receives the gift of God's love in
gratitude. As the Son of God, he became the one through
whom salvation comes to men. It was because of his love
for us that men could not tolerate him. Although he
brought life, they killed him. But God's purpose could not
be thwarted by brutality. He exalted Jesus to a position
of final authority and power, and called us to be the instruments by which his love can be carried to all men.
He gives us his Spirit to enable us to use every occasion as
an opportunity to demonstrate our deliverance from sin
and death.

"In the name of Jesus, therefore, we make known to all
men the same word which Jesus proclaimed: 'God has
acted. He has sent his Kingdom into your midst. Repent
and believe this good news. Then God will send his Spirit.
And the Spirit will give you eyes to see the Kingdom and
will bring you its peace.' Let us pray that we may be
ready to receive it."

The intense silence of prayer enveloped the worshipers.
Now and again the silence was broken by sharp ejacula-
tion, the Aramaic "Abba" or the Greek "Pater." Then the
phrase, "Come, Holy Spirit," was repeated several times,
until many were saying it in a unison chant. After a while

separate sentences could be distinguished. "Thy kingdom come." ... "Forgive us our sins." ... "Grant us our day's rations." ... "Deliver us from evil." One petitioner asked that Simon Peter and others might be released from prison to resume their work. Another prayed that they might all be prepared for any evil that might come. There were urgent petitions for the unbelievers present. It was more by common consent than by a leader's intervention that the period of prayer came to an end in a fervent series of amens. Nor did it seem to be by any conscious planning that the believers gradually changed from the praying to singing. The chant was different from the prayers only in its rhythmic cadence. It breathed the defiance of a proclamation and the buoyancy of a hymn:

"He lived above with God but did not pride himself on divine greatness and glory;
He gave up greatness and glory, taking instead the position of a slave, born like men, living like men.
He chose humility; he chose obedience, obedience to die, to die on the cross.
For this reason, God gave him glory,
Gave him a name above all names,
That at the name of Jesus every knee should bend
Of all above, beneath, and on the earth!
That at the name of Jesus every tongue confess to the glory of God that Jesus Christ is Lord."

The hymn completed, the tension relaxed and the worshipers arose and began to greet one another. Taking advantage of the interlude, Clement slipped out quietly and began retracing his path toward the center of the city. His spirit had been stirred by the genuineness of the praying and singing, but he was chagrined to find that his perplexities, instead of being satisfied, were aggravated.

Thinking back over what had been said, Clement realized that he had not even learned the speaker's name. He was disappointed, too, that he had learned so little about Jesus. Although these people were entirely convinced that Jesus had come in fulfillment of prophecy, there really seemed to be little that would support that conviction. The evidence of his authority, the signs that attested to it, were actually no more impressive than the answer that Peter had given to Bar-Joseph. In the cold light of realistic analysis, Bar-Joseph appeared fully justified in refusing on such circumstantial evidence to accept this man as Messiah.

And yet there was something else. A suspicion lurked in the corner of Clement's mind that this question could not be solved simply on the level of verbal statement or controversial argument. What was he to say about the authentic trust of these hunted people? Their enthusiasm could not be called artificial; their inner peace had the ring of iron, their positions echoed the confidence of men whose deepest needs have already been satisfied. Would illusions produce such faith? Was God actually speaking to them? And, what was more important, was God actually speaking through them to him? As he walked home from the house of Jonas, Clement wondered.

Near the Fire

ON THE following evening Clement arrived somewhat
earlier at the house of Jonas. The distance seemed
shorter, and he found himself less diffident and
more eager to probe the mysteries surrounding this new
community. This time as he came he resolved to ask more
questions of his own, questions which had been in his mind
for weeks. Though he no longer felt afraid of being caught
in the presence of disciples of Jesus, he had not been able
to bring himself to mention his new association to his
work mates or to Bar-Joseph.

He came up the steps to Jonas' apartment just as several
disciples were entering. This gave him an opportunity to
chat with them and to listen to their conversation. He was
introduced to Marcus, the speaker of the preceding night.
Marcus had just come from prison with the latest news
of Peter. Peter was still in custody. The officers would

neither release him nor indicate the charges on which he was held. He was not a prisoner of the regular police, but of Nero's secret service, a fact which made his fate subject more to the whims of the emperor than to regular legal procedures. To visit him was thus hazardous, but Marcus had been permitted to talk with him for a few minutes, and to give him a basket of food from the other disciples.

Clement asked Marcus how long he had known Peter. "A little over thirty years," was the answer. "My mother's home was in Jerusalem. I first heard the message about the Messiah from Peter one day when I was worshiping in the Temple. My mother and I both entered the Way, and for many years the disciples met at our home." Marcus became lost in reminiscence.

"Did you know Jesus?"

"No, it was about three years after his death that I first heard his name from Peter." Seeing that Clement was disappointed at this, he added: "But I met many people who had known him, and I heard from them many stories of his work. Before I became a disciple, I also talked with some of those who had opposed him."

Clement was still not satisfied. "Isn't there anyone in Rome who knew Jesus?"

Marcus thought a moment. "Peter is the only one left. You can talk with him if the police let him go."

The candid and direct spirit of Marcus invited a similar frankness from Clement. "You see," he said, "I am neither an opponent nor a disciple. I am quite bewildered by these claims you make for Jesus. I wish that I knew more about him."

"You are welcome to all that I know. I have traveled many places, first with my cousin Barnabas and Paul, and then with Peter. I have known many disciples. And I have heard many stories about Jesus and many of his teachings. In fact, I hope soon to write them down for the disciples here in Rome. If you can come early tomorrow evening, perhaps I can tell you some of them."

Clement could see that the meeting was about to begin. But he didn't want to lose the chance to raise the other major problem in his mind. "I'm also bewildered by the contradiction between what you say of Jesus' power to save men and the actual fact that Jesus himself was killed, his followers are jailed, and all of you are helpless to avoid execution. Does God save men by causing their death?"

The questions tumbled out in a heap, for they had long been twisting and churning in his mind. He could not escape them. Marcus noted the depth of concern and determined to answer as best he could. This was a problem that prevented many from accepting Jesus; it also constantly harassed disciples who found themselves tested, like Peter and the other prisoners who were even now being made to pay dearly for their constancy.

But the time had come for the service to start, and the apostle had to give a brief answer: "I'll touch on that problem tonight. And tomorrow night, if you come early, I will ask Jonas to show you a copy of a letter of Paul's in which he deals with your question."

The room, now crowded with people, became subdued in prayer. After the first rush of urgent petitions had subsided, Marcus arose. He began with a report on recent events.

"Tonight, as we worship here, our brothers are meeting in the houses of Aquila, Valerius Bito, and on Narcissus' estate. And in prison are seventeen others who in spirit are worshiping with us. Three of them are from this Church, four are from Aquila's group, seven are Narcissus' slaves, and three are from Valerius' home. All of us belong to one body—the body of Christ, living by the strength that he supplies. To the world we offer the word of salvation. We proclaim the Messiah as one who suffered for us. Thus has the prophecy of Isaiah come true:

> " 'Who has believed our message?
> To whom has God's arm been revealed?
> For he grew up like a young plant before us,
> Like a root out of dry ground:
> He had no attractive form to make us look at him.
> He had no beauty to make us desire him.
> He was despised and rejected by men;
> Afflicted by sorrow, familiar with sickness.
> Yet it was our sickness that he bore,
> Our sorrow that he carried;
> While we supposed that he was struck down,
> Afflicted by the command of God.
> But it was our sins for which he was wounded,
> It was our iniquities for which he was struck down;
> The chastisement of our peace was laid on him;
> With his stripes we are healed.
> All of us like sheep had turned away;
> We had turned to our own paths;
> And God has laid on him our guilt.' "

After this quotation Marcus paused. He wanted everyone to have a chance to let God speak through his prophecy. Finally he asked the simple question, "Of whom was God speaking?"

"Was he speaking of the Jews of Isaiah's day, of those who endured endless tortures for God's sake? Yes. Even then God's glory was being revealed through humble, despised men who preferred captivity and death to treason against God. In every generation, those who serve God must be acquainted with sorrow and familiar with grief. His arm is hidden from evil men who seek their own security. It is revealed to those who suffer. The prophets and martyrs of Israel have believed his message and remained faithful in death.

"But Isaiah also pointed ahead of him to Another who would suffer a like fate, an obedient Servant whom men would fail to recognize as one who would suffer for them. We disciples know that God has visited us in the form of Jesus. It is he who carries our sorrows. It is he whom we proclaim to the world as the Messiah. Let us review the story of his sacrifices for the sins of many. Let us confess how we, as well as others, have added to his sorrows.

"Last night I told the story of how God endowed Jesus with the Holy Spirit and with power, following the baptism which John had preached. Immediately after this baptism, the Spirit drove Jesus into the wilderness to be tempted. He was tested by all the devices by which the prince of evil seeks to deceive us and draw us away from the true path. Jesus was hungry, alone, obscure, a messenger with no credentials to impress men. And the tempter assailed him: 'If you would be Messiah, you must not be subject to hunger as other men are. Simply command these rocks to become loaves of bread, and you will have plenty to eat.' But Jesus saw through this deception, and answered, 'Man lives by obeying every word of God, not by bread alone.'

" 'How,' spoke the tempter, making a second effort, 'can you make yourself Messiah without showing to people some decisive sign of your power? Go to Jerusalem to the roof of the temple and jump off. It is written: 'He will give his angels a charge to protect you; they will bear you up, so that you will not be dashed against the stones.' But again Jesus saw what he was after, and resisted. 'Man shall not put God to such a test.'

"Finally the tempter tried his choice trick. He showed Jesus all the kingdoms of the world, in their power and magnificence: 'You are quite helpless to become the ruler of all men unless you accept my aid. Only by compromising with evil can goodness survive.' This time Jesus rebuked him and drove him away with the words: 'Thou shalt worship the Lord thy God. Him only shalt thou serve.'

"You will notice," continued Marcus, "that Satan chose to quote Scripture to support his strategy. He chose to appeal to prophecies which men, at Satan's suggestion, had come to associate with God's saving help. Surely a Messiah would have power to feed himself and his people, to avoid injury, and to command the glory of all the empires on earth. But such expectations are of Satan, and not of God. It was Jesus' obedience to God that enabled him to detect Satan's lure. And how did he do this? By listening to the true Word of God in the Law and the Prophets; by discerning therein the word and the worship by which men must live, to be true servants of God.

"It was through a will completely yielded to God that the Messiah was able to win this first battle, and in winning this battle he was winning the whole war for us. This meant that he would suffer, but God sent his angels, not to keep him from suffering, but to minister to him in his pain.

"But his temptations did not stop here, they kept striking him with increasing force. His obedience to God, however, gave him strength to resist and to fulfill the mission for which he was sent. Although Satan could not deceive our Messiah, he did deceive men about him. When the Messiah began to teach in his home synagogue, his neighbors could not accept him because he did not fit their ideas of what a Messiah must be. 'Where does he get this power and this wisdom?' they objected. 'This is a mere carpenter, Mary's son. We know his family.' It was to them that Jesus said, 'A prophet is not without honor, except in his own country, among his own relatives, and in his own house.'

"But Jesus also was tempted by the unbelief of his own disciples. Peter tells a story of how this happened. As his ministry in Galilee was drawing to a close, after he had been teaching and healing and proclaiming the good news of God's Kingdom, Jesus asked his disciples, 'Who do men say I am?' And they reported to him the different reactions. Some people were comparing him to John the Baptizer, some to Elijah or to one of the other prophets. Then Jesus asked point-blank, 'What do you say?' When Peter said in reply, 'Thou art the Christ,' Jesus began to explain that the Son of man must suffer and be rejected by the authorities and be killed. In horror Peter objected: 'No, Master, that surely cannot happen to you.' What did the Lord answer? He cried out: 'Let me alone, Satan. You do not consider God's way of doing things, but men's.' ·

"But let me tell you the story of the severest temptation of all. When Jesus came to Jerusalem, his disciples hailed him as Son of David, one through whom the Kingdom was about to come. But the holy city turned itself against its King. Scribes and elders, priests and rulers, rejected him. He came to the Temple to claim it as the house of his Father, but the priests took counsel how they might kill this troublemaker."

"Tell us the story of his death," asked Clement. "That would seem to be the center of the problem. I can see that the Messiah must battle with Satan. But how can one accept a Messiah whom Satan actually defeated?"

"This is the story, then," said Marcus, "the story which every disciple knows by heart. It is the story of Satan's power, or so it will seem. But it is also the story of an innocent Man who was slain for our sin.

"It was two days before the festival of the Passover was to be held that the religious authorities plotted to arrest Jesus and put him to death—not, of course, actually during the festival, lest riots break out. Judas Iscariot, one of Jesus' companions, came to the priests with an offer to place Jesus in their power. They accepted the offer gladly and promised him a cash reward. Judas began watching for a suitable opportunity to betray Jesus into their hands.

"But Jesus knew what was happening. One evening he was eating with his followers. In the middle of the meal Jesus said, 'I am about to be betrayed by one of you.' A sudden gloom fell on them, and they asked him: 'Who is it? Is it I?' He answered: 'It is one of you eating with me. The Deliverer must suffer as was foretold of him, but woe to the man through whom the Deliverer is betrayed! It would be better for him if he had never been born.' Then, while they were eating, he took a loaf into his hands and gave thanks; then he broke it and gave it to them, saying, 'Take this; it is my body.' Then he took a cup into his hand and gave thanks for it. He passed it to them and they all drank. He said: 'This is the pledge of a new covenant with God. Indeed, I shall not taste wine again until the time comes when I shall drink it with you in the kingdom of God.' Then they finished supper, sang a hymn, and went out to the Hill of Olives.

"Here Jesus warned them again: 'All of you will be tempted to deny me. The prophets have said that when the shepherd is struck down his flock will scatter in all directions. Yet, even so, I shall be raised up again, and when you return to Galilee, you will find me there.' But Peter protested. 'Even if all the rest fail you, I will not.' Then Jesus said, 'You yourself will disown me three times this very night.' But Peter protested all the more vigorously. 'Even if the price of my loyalty to you is death, I will remain faithful to you.' And they all agreed.

"It was then that Judas Iscariot came up with an armed crowd, sent by the priests. The traitor had arranged a signal with them: 'I shall kiss the man you want.' So Judas approached Jesus and greeted him with a kiss. The escort seized him at once. One of Jesus' friends drew a sword and aimed a blow at one of the party and cut off his ear. But Jesus struck no blow. He merely said to them: 'Why this armed force as if I were a man of violence? I've been teaching you every day in the temple and you could easily have taken me then.' Then all his friends scattered as fast as they could. So Jesus was taken to the chief priest, who held a hearing to decide what should be done with him.

"Peter, who had returned to follow Jesus at a safe distance, came in as far as the vestibule. One of the servant girls noticed him there. She looked at him closely and then said, 'You too were with that man from Nazareth.' But Peter denied it and said, 'I don't know what you're talking about.' The girl began making remarks about him to those who stood around: 'He's one of them.' Peter again denied it. Later someone else said to him, 'You belong to that lot right enough; you're from Galilee too.' And he began to swear that he didn't know whom they were talking about. No sooner had the words left his lips than the cock crew a second time, and in a flash the warning of Jesus came back to him: 'You will disown me.' And he went away, shaking with sobs.

"In the morning the priests decided to have Jesus bound again as a prisoner and handed him over to the Roman governor, Pilate. When Pilate asked him whether he was the King of the Jews, Jesus replied, 'So you say.' The priests brought many charges against Jesus, and Pilate asked, 'Why don't you make a defense against these accusations?' But Jesus remained silent. Then Pilate handed over Jesus to be flogged, and after that to be put on a cross. So the soldiers led him away. They dressed him up in a cloak of royal purple and put a crown on his head—a crown of thorns which they had twisted. And they walked up and down past him, saluting him as King of the Jews. They hit him about the head with a stick and spat at him. After they had gone on with this mockery for some time, they let Jesus put on his own clothes again and then led him out to be crucified.

"It was mid-morning when Jesus was nailed to the cross. Above him was written out the title by which he was accused: 'The King of the Jews.' There were two convicts crucified at the same time, one on each side of him. Passers-by made fun of him. 'So you're the fellow who claimed to tear down the temple and build it up again in three days; very well, save yourself and get off that cross.' The priests joked about him amongst themselves: 'He saved others; he can't save himself. If he's the Messiah, why doesn't he come down from the cross? That would convince us.' And then Jesus shouted out, 'Eloi, Eloi, lama sabachthani,' which means, 'My God, my God, why have you forsaken me?' Some of the onlookers said, 'Listen, he's calling Elijah'; and one of them hurried to get a sponge and dipped it in some sour wine and put it up on the end of a stick for Jesus to drink, saying, 'Give him a chance; let's see if Elijah will come and take him down.' But Jesus gave another loud cry and died.

"This is the climax," continued Marcus, "of the story of Jesus' temptation, and this very suffering was the proof of Jesus' obedience. He carried his obedience so far as to die, and to die the death of the cross. This was the hour of darkness, when Satan seemed supreme, when all men were tempted by the world's standard of power—all men, that is, except the Messiah. It was thus that Jesus fulfilled Isaiah's prophecy:

" 'When he was oppressed, he humbled himself
    without protest.
Through violence and judgment he was taken away;
And no one realized that he was cut off for our
    transgressions.
They made his grave with the wicked, his tomb
    with workers of evil,
Although he had done no violence,
And there was no deceit in his mouth.'

"But this, thank God, was not the end of the story. It
was the point at which God made known that this Jesus is
Lord of all.

"Let me report to you now the message which Peter
sent to all of you today."

Clement leaned forward with great intentness, and he
noticed that the others present were sitting on the edges
of their chairs. The narration of the death of Jesus had
caught them in a spell, but now it seemed as if they had all
stopped breathing. Even Marcus was gripped by the tension, and began speaking more slowly, as if the fate of
every disciple was bound up with the fate of Peter.

"I asked him if he was afraid of what lay ahead of him
and whether he had the strength to endure. 'Marcus,' he
said, 'whenever I am tempted by suffering to disown our
Lord, I remember those times in Galilee and in Jerusalem
when my faith cracked, and I remember how Jesus looked
at me and loved me in spite of my cowardice. I recall too
that night of Jesus' death, when my knees turned to water
and I fled from dangers which he accepted so calmly.
Most of all, however, there comes back to me the scene
at the lake in Galilee, after the Crucifixion. We disciples
had given up, and were back in the boat fishing. But our
hearts weren't in the fishing, and we kept talking, in ach-
ing despair, about how our hopes had crumbled and how
God had forsaken us. I think that deep in our hearts

we knew that we had been faithless to God, but we were aware only of a haunting feeling that God had been faithless to us. None of us knew what to do.

"Then he appeared to us. We saw him in his heavenly glory, white and dazzling. He came toward us and called us to the shore. He broke bread with us and explained to us why his Father had led him to the cross. The cross is the road to the Kingdom, he explained, and it was necessary for the Messiah to take that road so that men like us might also find it. He made clear to us that God had not forsaken him, but had been faithful in death itself. He asked us how much we loved him. This time I could only stammer, 'Depart from me, for I am a sinful man, O Lord.' But he answered: 'Follow me along the road I have taken. I have chosen you to be my witness. You must carry the message of God's salvation to the whole world. Do not be afraid, for I will go with you and sustain you.'"

Marcus paused, and the disciples relaxed. Then he continued quietly: "Peter told me that since that morning when the risen Lord called him, God has never allowed him to be tempted beyond his power to resist. And today Peter said with joy that the Messiah had never been so close and so real. He told me to give you this word from Jesus: 'The disciple who endures to the end will be saved.'"

The suspense that had gripped the disciples was relieved at last, and they sank to their knees. All their prayers seemed to be variations on the same theme—joy, gratitude, and confidence fused into an ecstatic praise of the Lord's goodness. "Blessed art thou, O Lord, who hast opened to us the way of salvation." . . . "Blessed art thou, O Lord, who hast given us a portion in the Messiah's suffering." . . . "Blessed art thou, O Lord, who forgivest our sins and healest our wounds." . . . "God sent his Son to suffer for us." . . . "Hallelujah." . . . "Hallelujah."

Soon the scattered ejaculations of "Hallelujah" merged into one song in which all the disciples joined:

> "Blessing and honor, glory and power
> Be given him who sits upon the throne
> And to the Lamb that was slain,
> And by his death ransomed us from sin.
> Hallelujah."

Clement was afraid of the powerful contagion of this group ecstasy, and took advantage of the moment to move unnoticed out of the door. He found himself perspiring from the inner ordeal of listening to such confident faith when his own mind was churning with conflicting emotions. He had sensed the magnetic pull of their faith, but at the same time had become more and more fearful. At several points in Marcus' address he had felt his feet being swept out from under him by the strong tide. Now, walking home through the cool air, he was glad that he had not lost his balance. He was glad that he could now control the pace of his thoughts, and not be hurried too fast by these impetuous Christians. If one is to accept a faith that involves crucifixion, he should certainly be level-headed and look carefully before taking the first step.

At least, he thought, *these folk are honest with themselves and others. They don't offer diamonds at the price of pebbles. In fact, they seem to try to frighten men away by their promise of suffering. Do they want to be martyrs? Does their Messiah offer nothing but death? That indeed would be a gruesome solution to the problems of life.*

Freed from the pressures of the meeting, all his objections began to reassert themselves with new force. He knew intuitively that he had been very close to the fire, and that he had barely escaped without getting burned.

CHAPTER 10

Two Letters

CLEMENT did not return to Jonas' house the next night to read Paul's letter and to talk more with Marcus about Jesus. Underneath all his thoughts and feelings lay an instinctive dread of any further contact with the Christians. He was aware that he had averted a terrible fate by a narrow margin. The vivid contrast between that experience and the next day's activity made him feel as if he had emerged from a period of hypnosis.

On his way to work that morning, Clement savored with fresh delight the bright colors and crisp air of autumn. Nature had put on her most gorgeous dress, and by contrast the atmosphere of the Christian meeting seemed, in retrospect, gray and gloomy.

Yes, he thought, *it is unnatural for people to become so obsessed with the evils of the world. Life isn't so intoler-*

able as all that. Why should I take the zest out of life by spending my evenings with a group of fanatics?

In fact, he was inwardly pleased to discover how easily he could throw off the spell which the Christians had woven about his thoughts. He tackled the masonwork with a vim that surprised both Julian and Lentulus. *What moods this fellow has!* thought Lentulus. *Until now he has been glum and uninteresting. But today he is lively and gay.* Clement's vigor and good spirits infected his work mates, and the walls seemed to rise with twice their former speed.

The enthusiasm persisted, and before many days had passed, Sabinus noticed the improved morale and commented favorably on the progress of the work. He was happy to find the construction ahead of schedule, and he brought out the plans for the next building to be erected. He asked advice from the masons on the kind of stone to be ordered and invited them to suggest improvements in design. Then he casually dropped a remark that instantly aroused their fancy:

"You know, boys, if you keep up this pace until the second house is done, I may lend your services to the emperor. He is looking for expert masons to help on his new palace."

All three leaped at the opportunity. What could be more thrilling than to work on the most elaborate house in Rome? It would give them a chance to know everything about Nero's home and to impress the emperor himself with their skill.

With their ambitions pegged at this high level, they began to work together with greater energy than ever. They even agreed to work overtime in the evenings to impress Sabinus. They also began a more systematic study of other buildings under construction, noting the quality of materials, the different kinds of tools, and the designs of the carpenters. This enabled them to suggest several improvements in the sketch of Sabinus' house and short cuts in the labor. Clement, for example, showed Sabinus how they could make the windows wider and thus provide a better view of the gardens. By selecting the stones more carefully, it would be possible too to bring out more interesting patterns of color.

They became more interested in architectural styles, of which the city offered a great variety. They studied carefully the lines of public buildings and noted mistakes that other builders had made. Their interest took them into the temples, with their lofty colonnades and colorful mosaics. Clement, to be sure, felt a twinge of conscience on being engaged in such pursuits, since his father had nurtured in him a strong feeling against statues and pagan priests. Nevertheless, his heart was so ambitious that his conscience was easily overruled.

Now that the city's strangeness had worn off and a bright prospect beckoned, Clement was less inclined to be critical of everything pagan. He almost began to think of himself as a Roman, and a heady feeling it was. Whereas he had thought of soldiers as merciless adversaries, he now was attracted by the magnificence of a company fully armed and marching in orderly ranks.

One day an official holiday was scheduled, to be celebrated by chariot racing. Lentulus urged his friends to go with him. Both Julian and Clement had some qualms, but they were afraid of displeasing their friend, and, besides, the show was free. So they spent the day together at the Circus. The boys loved horses, and they were fascinated by the speed of the two-horse chariots and by the frequent spills in the arena. Lentulus supported the Blues, both vocally and by wagers. Of the four stables represented, the Blues and the Greens seemed to have the edge. There were twenty separate races in all, and as the day went by the lead passed back and forth between these two stables. When the last race began, the score was tied. And when the Blue chariot came in ahead by a yard, the whole stadium turned into a howling mob. Lentulus had won a large profit and was as hilarious as anyone present. Clement was completely absorbed in watching the carnival and the half-crazed mob. "So this is Rome," he kept saying to himself and to Julian.

These intense activities so occupied Clement that he almost forgot that he was a Jew. Each evening he was reminded of it when he returned to his lodgings. But each morning he left these associations behind when he went to work. It even occurred to him to look for a room with a Gentile family near the Esquiline. Then he would be spared this nightly reminder. His evenings would be freer and he and Julian could make their plans for the future more effectively.

When the Sabbath came, Clement was almost too tired to attend the synagogue service, although the habit of being present was not one that he could easily break. But the service exerted less power over him. The prayers seemed too long, and Clement began to suspect that most worshipers were quite content with formal observance of the customs of the past. For some reason he had lost the inclination to meditate on the Scripture or on the benedictions. In fact, he held himself aloof from the whole service, lest he might become involved again in problems that could only disturb him.

One night, on returning to Bar-Joseph's home, Clement found a letter waiting from his father. Seeing it brought suddenly and sharply to his mind a picture of his home and family and the world he had left behind. So many things had been happening that he had almost forgotten what his last letter home had dealt with.

*　　*　　*

MATTATHIAS TO HIS SON CLEMENT, GREETING:

I rejoice that you are so well situated in Rome and that your work is starting well. We miss you at home, and especially at this season of harvest. But we shall manage. I thank our God that you have found friends in the Synagogue of the Olive Tree. God's house is the only house where one can find peace and strength. And you will find that his Word is able to fulfill all your needs. Your life in the city is a major test of your loyalty, not to your family alone, but, more important, to God's household. [Here a deep uneasiness stirred in Clement's conscience.]

You ask my advice about this announcement of the Messiah which you have recently heard. It is true that God will deliver us from our suffering, in his own time and way. We must wait patiently for him to bring his salvation. Our trust in his promises is our only excuse for existence as a separate people. But I am very skeptical about these reports that the Messiah is now at hand. We have suffered too much from false messiahs who accomplish nothing, but only increase our frustration and arouse the fears of our enemies. The more desperate Israel's plight, the more impatient become these agitators for the end of the age.

I would urge you, then, to go very slowly in accepting vain dreams as signs of more than discontented and disordered minds, looking for hasty escape from the lot to which God has assigned us. Let me suggest that you test their messages very carefully.

Is the prophet interested in inciting military action against oppressors? If so, shun him like the plague. He will lead us only into a more galling slavery. Does the prophet use his message to finance himself or to attract attention to himself? Then he will use you only to advance his own prestige. Does he make the way of obedience easier by relaxing the requirements of the Law, by breaking down the barriers between Israel and the world, further defiling Israel? Does he himself obey the Law?

Our people have secured their legacy by patience, long-suffering, and sacrifice. We must not be tempted by any short cut to salvation to surrender that legacy. God's promises are not vain; he will fulfill them. We must live according to his Word. And whatever more we need, he will reveal to us in his own time.

But I need not write these things to you. You yourself have been taught in our Holy Scriptures. If you meet with doubt, Bar-Joseph and the other elders will instruct you.

Your mother and brothers send greetings. Express our gratitude to Bar-Joseph for his hospitality, and return my greetings to Jason, Ezra, and Sabinus. It may be that in the spring I shall be able to leave my duties here for a visit in the city. God's blessing be yours.

*   *   *

His father's letter made Clement realize how far away from home and synagogue he had drifted. He was in no mood to give up his new freedom and zest, yet he could not escape the awareness that he was by no means so happy in his recent infatuation with Roman life as he had supposed. Back of his surface thoughts spoke a quiet voice: *Fool, you are not so free as you think. You cannot change skins so quickly. Your heart is not in this thing.*

The letter also revived another source of discomfort— his recent interest in the Christians. Was it only a week since he had been at Jonas' house? Then he had been completely engrossed in their story about Jesus, as if the Crucifixion had just taken place. But now it all seemed remote —far away and long ago. Yet as he thought of the people he had met at Jonas' house, he could not keep down a certain concern about them. *What has happened to Peter?* he wondered. *And to Marcus and the others? Are they still meeting every evening in that strange, exalted atmos-*

phere? What's to prevent my going back tomorrow night? At least I can find what has taken place during this week. And now that I know what I want to do in Rome, I won't be so susceptible to their enthusiasm. My feet are on solid ground, and the fervor of the group won't carry me away. Perhaps Julian will go with me, and then we can talk about our reactions after the meeting. I can think about the questions that father asked about the prophet, and send him an impartial report. He will be interested.

As Clement pondered his father's tests, he knew that some of them had already been met by the followers of Jesus. These men were not wild-eyed radicals, bent on stirring up violent rebellion against Rome. Nor were they spellbinders, greedy for prestige, popularity, and financial gain from the gullible and superstitious masses. There remained, then, only the test of their faithfulness to the Scriptures. Would their message result in undermining the Law and destroying Israel's sacred institutions? Yes, Clement would raise these problems and would send his father the answers.

When morning came, Clement changed his mind about inviting Julian. After all, he would probably be unsympathetic toward the Christians and would be bored. There was no need to tell him about the meeting. The decision proved to be a wise one, for when Clement arrived at the house on the Appian Way he found it quiet. *Have they all been arrested?* he wondered.

When he knocked, a woman opened the door. After an exchange of greetings, she introduced herself as Jonas' wife, Della. No, there would be no gathering this evening. Peter had urged the group to begin the work of preaching in various parks in the city, and they had divided up into groups to accompany the speakers. There would be a service the following evening, and he was heartily invited to return. Della remembered Clement from the previous week and talked freely with him.

In reply to his question, she said that Peter was still in prison and nothing had been decided about his fate. No others had been arrested. When Clement told her of Marcus' suggestion that he read Paul's letter, she brought out a copy of it. The scroll was crumpled and worn, showing frequent use. Della explained that after Paul had been killed, several copies of his letter had been made so that each of the Roman Churches could have one. She herself had known Paul and she was able to give Clement a brief characterization of the apostle. Then she left him alone to study the scroll.

How fortunate! he thought. *I can perhaps find out the answers to my father's questions without meeting the whole group and disturbing their worship.*

Clement did not at first relish the thought of reading an intimate personal letter intended for others. But this mood quickly passed. Having seen the Christian community in Rome, he was surprised at the great esteem in which Paul held this Roman Church. "Word of your faith has spread all over the world." How strange that a group still virtually unknown in Rome should be praised thus! The apostle seemed to include both Jews and Gentiles in his message, expressing his personal indebtedness to both. "Salvation," he wrote, "is equally open to both. The good news is God's power to save everyone who believes, the Jew first and then the Greek." So faith in Jesus as God's Son was more important in gaining salvation than the distinction between Jew and Greek! Clement knew that his father would take offense at that.

Reading farther, however, Clement found the most stinging attack upon the Gentiles he had ever heard. The words were still blistering-hot: "fools," "shameless," "heart-

less," "ruthless," "God-haters." What a speaker this man
must have been, who could scorch his hearers with such
epithets! The lines reminded Clement of Peter's speech in
the Forum. *Even my father doesn't indulge in such tirades,*
he thought. *It's no wonder that Paul made enemies. Here
he says, for example, that they all deserve to die.*

The next section of the letter was even more astounding,
for Paul now turned a more withering fire against the
Jews: Jews, to be sure, possess certain advantages, but
these advantages make their guilt all the heavier. They
claim to be superior through knowing God's Law, but in
fact none of them have kept that Law. They are condemned by their own Law as thieves, adulterers, blas-
phemers. Their circumcision is valid only if they obey the
Law; since none of them obey it, they are all inwardly
uncircumcised, all under condemnation as sinners, all facing terrible wrath. *So that's the story,* thought Clement.
*This man claims that there is no distinction between me
and the worst Gentile, or between my father and Nero.
Yes, father is right in this: Paul's message clearly destroys
the separation between Israel and the world. This unknown Jew, in his bitterness, has declared war on the
whole human race, accusing everyone as being engaged in
a hopeless fight against God.*

*What has happened to lead a man to such despair? If
the situation is so hopeless, what is left for a man to do?
How could he suppose that men would listen to him, if
he began by destroying their faith in themselves?*

Clement was ready to return the scroll to Jonas' wife,
content that this was no more than the cynical raving of a
man who scorned everyone. But something made him
pause. Somewhere within him throbbed a nerve that kept
pricking. Suddenly he recalled his discussion with Julian
about the dilemma of a just man in an unjust world. They

had talked about Seneca and about the Jewish heroes, wondering why the good man always suffers. Had they not actually despaired over the world, with its brutalities and debaucheries? Was Paul's description perhaps more accurate than men cared to admit?

Then too he kept wondering *why* this letter should condemn everyone so completely. *Does Paul have something else in reserve? Why does God place men in this predicament? Paul had begun by appealing to God's power to save both Jew and Greek. How is this possible if everyone is so sinful?*

He did not need to read much farther to get a glimpse at the answer. According to this writer, God has intended to close the roads which Jew and Greek followed in order to open a new road. He revealed this new road in Jesus the Messiah. Apart from him, all are lost. But through him, all may be saved. Though all men have sinned and are under condemnation, God loves all men equally and has disclosed this love by sending his Son to die for men, while they were still sinners. Now, the man who recognizes his own helplessness and trusts God's love completely can start life again on a new basis. Accepting God's forgiveness, he can be freed from despair and condemnation. He can begin again as a son of Abraham, a member of the family to whom God fulfills his promises. This new road means suffering (Clement thought again of Peter), but it also means joy and hope and love. Those who follow the Messiah on this new road receive the Holy Spirit as a constant companion.

Here Clement checked himself. He did not know what these words meant. Paul was writing about something that Clement had never experienced. What joy could flood a person's life in the midst of suffering? What was this Holy Spirit that is said to accompany one? Such words tantalized him, as a traveler returning from a distant country might tantalize his hearers by describing strange animals they had never seen. Clement could not tell whether these things actually existed or not. *Perhaps this author is crazy; perhaps he is spinning an incredible yarn. At any rate, he is using a language foreign to me.* He rolled up the letter without finishing it and returned it to Della. Bidding her good night, he began his walk homeward.

On the way, the ideas in the letter kept simmering in his mind. He recalled the story of Jesus' death, as told by Peter and Marcus, the story of an innocent Prophet rejected by everyone and dying alone on a cross. So this was the gist of what these Christians called good news: the announcement that God loves the worst sinner so much as to sacrifice the Messiah to open the Kingdom to sinners. To enter the Kingdom it is not necessary that the sinner first become wise or good. All he needs to do is to admit his guilt, lay aside his pride, accept this crucified carpenter as Messiah, and follow him. Jews and Gentiles are lost when they try to win salvation on their own terms. First they try to achieve wisdom or goodness; then they expect God to approve and reward their efforts. And this road leads only to frustration.

The Christians insist that God has set very different terms. God seeks above everything else to deflate men's complacency and self-sufficiency. A man can share God's love only when he accepts God's terms.

Now Clement could see clearly how startling and daring this whole position was. Paul was not attacking simply his father and Bar-Joseph, or Nero and the more vicious pagans. He was pitted against the whole human race. He was seeking to undermine the confidence which men had, not only in the synagogue and the Law, but also in all Gentile institutions as well. Surely in saying such things he was inviting men everywhere to reject him, just as the authorities in Palestine had rejected Jesus. But he was also inviting these same men to follow the Messiah, as the only one who could save men. What would impel a man to do this? Did Paul hate men, or did he love them? If the Christians were right, was it fair for God to set such terms for men to follow?

Had Clement been forced at that moment to answer this last question, he would have said, "No." What Paul was saying offended him and troubled him. It seemed too harsh, and there were too many things about it that he did not understand—too much vagueness about the promise of joy and peace. Yet he was inwardly excited by the issue which had been posed so sharply. Paul's letter had given his mind a more vigorous diet than anything he had ever read.

CHAPTER 11

The Price of Peace

LENTULUS and Julian wanted to work overtime the next night, but Clement declined. "An errand for my father," was his way of excusing himself. The boys were disgruntled, for the whole day had been marred by the tiny cracks that had developed in the smooth surface of their friendship. Clement had been absent-minded and listless; Julian had begun to doubt whether he really wanted the assignment to Nero's employ; and Lentulus' temper had become quite ragged. Clement could have mended the friction by staying on with his mates, but something made him stubborn and he left promptly at quitting time.

Of course, his excuse was true. He did need to be able to answer his father's query about the Christians. Why did they treat so casually the duty of Law observance and Temple worship? He still could not put the answer in his

127

own words to his own satisfaction. And how could he satisfy himself until he had questioned Marcus further?

By now, however, he was dimly conscious that he was
involved in a deeper problem—whether or not he himself
could ignore or escape the sharp point of their message.
It would be cowardly to retreat until he could give a better answer to himself and to the Christians, wholly apart
from answering his father. Inwardly, he felt very restless
and ill at ease. They had succeeded at least to this extent:
until he could satisfy himself as to the falsity of what they
called the Gospel, he could never be confident of the basis
of his own life.

At the evening meeting he was greeted with the usual
cordiality. A larger number of inquirers than usual were
on hand. He noted that many were Jews, and he felt that
frank questions on the superiority of the Christians over
the Jews would be in order. He would imagine his father
as present and propose such questions as Mattathias would
offer, that is, if he could think of them at the right time.

As on former occasions, the meeting began with spontaneous praying and adoration, the disciples urging the
Holy Spirit to touch their eyes and lips and hearts. Then
Marcus led the group in benedictions, to each of which
the worshipers gave hearty response. Clement recognized
the first two as customary in the synagogue, and was almost moved to join in the responses.

MARCUS: "Blessed art thou, O Lord our God and God of
    our fathers;
    God of Abraham, God of Isaac, God of Jacob;
    The great, mighty and revered God,
    Creator of heaven and earth,
    Our shield and the shield of our fathers,
    Our confidence from generation to generation."
PEOPLE: "Blessed art thou, O Lord, the shield of Abraham."

MARCUS: "Thou art mighty, and bringest low the proud;
Thou art strong, and judgest the ruthless;
Thou art he that liveth forever, that raiseth the dead;
That maketh the wind to blow, that sendeth down the dew;
That sustaineth the living, that quickeneth the dead;
In the twinkling of an eye, thou dost make salvation to spring forth for us."

PEOPLE: "Blessed art thou, O Lord, who dost quicken the dead."

To these prayers from the familiar benedictions, Clement noticed that two new ones were added.

MARCUS: "Blessed art thou, O Lord, God and Father of our Lord Jesus Christ!
By thy great mercy hast thou brought us again to a living hope through the resurrection of Jesus Christ from the dead."

PEOPLE: "Blessed art thou, O Lord, who hast granted us this living hope."

MARCUS: "Blessed art thou, O Lord, who hast laid up in heaven an imperishable inheritance for us who by thy power are guarded through faith, for a salvation ready to be revealed."

PEOPLE: "Blessed art thou, O Lord, who hast granted us this unfading inheritance. Amen."

Then Marcus began his address: "God has promised men life. That promise he has fulfilled in our midst, for he has raised Jesus from the dead, and has in him established a new creation. Born again into this new life, we bless him.

"Long ago God promised Israel deliverance from bondage and redemption from slavery. That promise he has fulfilled in our midst, for he has called us out of darkness into light, and transferred us from the kingdom of Satan to the Kingdom of his Son. Heirs of this new Kingdom, we bless him."

Then, turning his eyes to the newcomers, he spoke slowly: "Men of Israel, listen to our testimony. We disciples are not enemies of the synagogue, but this Church is the real synagogue which God has established. True, we have been cast out of most buildings now called synagogues, but even this is God's doing.

"Recall the prophecy from long ago: 'After these things I will return, and I will build again the tabernacle of David, which is fallen; and I will build again its ruins, that men may seek after the Lord, including the Gentiles upon whom my name is called.'

"But you may say that the Temple has not been destroyed. Of course, there is a building still standing in Jerusalem where our brothers worship. That is not, however, the true Temple. Of that Temple our Messiah said that not one stone should be left on another. When he tried to restore it to the true worship of God, the Temple authorities defended themselves by killing him. Since then, the Messiah has been establishing the true Temple wherever men worship God in his spirit. We are the temple of God, if we live by faith in his Son. Jesus sends his Spirit to dwell in us, and to direct our hearts in praising God."

Clement interrupted the speaker. "It seems to me, Marcus, that you follow a queer strategy if you hope to make converts of us Jews. Must you antagonize us by such direct attacks upon our holiest possessions such as the Temple? You Christians seem to have a chip on your shoulder, trying to prove that all others are deluded and sinful."

"It is not we who condemn such possessions," was the rejoinder. "The Law and the Prophets themselves make clear how far men have betrayed God in using these holy possessions. What is the Law, which we Jews have accepted as our yoke? Is it not to do the will of God? What is the First Commandment? Is it not to love God with our whole heart? Have we done that, or merely fooled ourselves into thinking that we were doing it? Those who killed Jesus thought that they were serving God, but they were actually serving Satan. Was it not on this very charge that Moses and the prophets accused the men of Israel? 'This people honors me with their lips, but their heart is set against me. In vain they worship me, teaching as their doctrines the precepts of men.'

"Let me repeat for you a parable which the Messiah gave us:

> " 'Two men went to the temple to pray; one was a Pharisee, the other a publican. The Pharisee stood and prayed thus with himself: God, I thank thee that I am not like so many men, extortioners, unjust, adulterers, or even like this publican. I fast twice a week, I give a tenth of all I get. The publican, standing far at the back, would not even lift his eyes to heaven, but struck his chest, saying, God, be merciful to me a sinner! I tell you that this man went away justified, rather than the other.'

"To the Pharisee the good news seems like bad news, for it tells him, 'You are not so good as you think. You cannot claim any special righteousness. In fact, your case is hopeless so long as you are blind to your own sin.' Only the sinner can see how good this news is, for he does not blind himself to his own desperate situation. When he hears that God loves him so much as to die for him, while he is still a sinner—when he believes this message in his heart, he prays for God's forgiveness and receives peace."

"Then you claim that this publican is superior in God's sight to the man who carefully fulfills all his religious duties?" Clement was insistent, because he had to get this point straight.

"Let me answer as Jesus answered, with a parable.

"'A man had two sons. He came to the first and said, Son, go work today in the vineyard. And he answered, I will not, but afterward he changed his mind and went. Then he came to the second and said the same thing. This son answered, I go, sir. But he did not go. Which of the two did the will of his father?'"

"It would be hard to object to the logic of that story," admitted Clement. "But how can one know that you Christians are all fully obedient, and the Jews in the synagogue are not? You condemn them for claiming to be superior to publicans and harlots. But don't you fall into the same trap by calling yourselves superior to them? Doesn't that make you as boastful and hypocritical as they?"

"God forbid," declared Marcus. "We can never consider ourselves superior. That is the chief trouble with the world. Romans look down upon Greeks; Greeks despise men from Asia; senators snub the knights; and free men sneer at slaves. Everyone lives in a false world where he feeds his pride by such comparisons. That's just the sort of boasting that God has destroyed on the cross. He has chosen the lowest, most helpless men to put to shame the great and powerful. No true disciple can feel superior to any other person, for he knows that apart from God's love he would be worthless.

"Listen to this word from Jesus:

"'Those who rule over Gentiles lord it over them. The great men exercise authority over them. But it is different among you. Whoever would be great among you must be least of all; whoever would be first among you must be servant of all. For the Son of man came not to be served but to serve, and to give his life a ransom for many.'

"A disciple cannot count himself superior to others. In fact, he does not compare himself with others at all but only with his Master, who always chose to be least of all and Servant of all. The disciple sees his own sinfulness and worthlessness so clearly that his interest is in finding forgiveness and peace with God for himself and others.

"Listen to another parable that shows how joy comes when a man repents.

" 'What man who has a hundred sheep, of which one gets lost, will not leave the ninety-nine in the wilderness, and search for the one that is lost, until he finds it? And when he has recovered it, he joyfully carries it home. Then he calls his friends and neighbors, saying to them, Rejoice with me, for I have found my sheep. In the same way there is joy in heaven over one sinner who repents.' "

Then Marcus turned to the inquirers with a direct appeal: "Admit that you are not able to save yourselves. Repent and let God save you. Forsake this age and follow the Messiah, whom God has sent to proclaim forgiveness of your sin and to lead you into his Kingdom. The promise is to you. What answer will you give to God?"

"It all seems too easy," said another inquirer, taking the initiative. "You say that all one needs to do is to repent. How can a simple step like that produce such great results? A single change of mind, a shift of moods, and you say the thing is done. Anything so simple cannot be worth much. I sometimes wish one could find satisfaction and peace that quickly. You seem to picture life as a jungle in which everyone is lost, but one yard from each weary person is a short cut that would take him suddenly out of the whole maze! Sounds like a pleasant dream. If only it were true!"

"But it is true," Marcus answered. "That's why it is such good news. One moment, one decision, makes all the difference. No matter where you are or who you are, you can repent. You don't have to wait until all the world's sicknesses are cured, until you are wiser than others, or until you have proved yourself worthy of God's help. But don't deceive yourself into thinking salvation is cheap or easy. It cost God his only Son. And you cannot tell what it may cost you if you cast in your lot with him. For repentance is, in a way, self-inflicted death. Let me explain what I mean.

"If you repent, you must say no to all thought of your own superiority, and who wants to do that? We would rather believe the lie that we are good men than to accept God's judgment that we are sinners. You must stop relying on your own private hopes, your special ambition to become someone important, and who wants to do that? You must give up all security in this world, trusting only in what God chooses to give you, and who wants to do that? You must accept ridicule and hatred from others—your relatives and friends and those who have power over you, and who wants to do that? If you repent, you must share the very burden which Christ himself carried, becoming servant of all as well as least of all. A Christian has no power over himself once he becomes the possession of Christ.

"This is his command: 'If anyone would be my disciple, let him deny himself, take up his cross, and follow along my road. Whoever tries to save his life will lose it; whoever loses his life for my sake will save it.'

"Jesus gave a parable to frighten away those who look for easy solutions:

" 'Which of you who desires to build a tower does not first sit down and figure the cost to see if he has enough money to complete it? Otherwise, when he has laid a foundation, and has run out of funds, men will mock him, saying, The fool began to build but was not able to finish.'

"No one can be a disciple of Jesus unless within his own heart he has already made an unconditional surrender of everything he has and is.

"Ask any of us," continued Marcus. "We will tell you what it costs to put to death our own fears and hopes, our own place in the world, our own self-centeredness, our own pride. But we will also tell you that the Messiah makes these sacrifices easy. He shares with us his courage and strength, and gives us so much to live for that we do not care about what we have had to give up. To repent, you must dive into the stream of suffering, but in that stream you will be buoyed up by the deep current of God's love and joy.

"It is the Messiah who invites you into the ranks of his followers. If his voice reaches you, stay with us after the meeting:

"'Come to me, you who are burdened and tired,
  I will give you rest.
  Carry my yoke, learn of me;
    for I am meek and humblehearted,
  and you will find rest.
  For my yoke is easy, my burden is light.'"

The prayers were spontaneous and filled with gratitude. As Clement fidgeted at the back of the room, waiting for a chance to leave, the prayers, like javelins, seemed to penetrate the protective shell around his heart. "I thank thee, Father, that thy yoke is easy." . . . "God be merciful to me a sinner." . . . "Blessed art thou, God, for thou hast forgiven me." One of the disciples, in a tone of triumph, repeated a familiar prayer:

"'Now let thy servant depart, Lord,
  According to thy word, in peace;
  For mine eyes have seen thy salvation
  Which thou hast prepared before the face of all peoples,
  A light for revelation to the Gentiles,
  And the glory of thy people Israel.'"

These individual confessions and prophecies were finally blended with one concluding chant:

> "Blessed be the Lord, the God of Israel,
> For he has visited and wrought redemption for his people,
> And has raised up a horn of salvation for us
> In the house of his servant David
> (As he spake by the mouth of his holy prophets that have been from of old),
> Salvation from our enemies, and from the hand of all that hate us;
> To show mercy toward our fathers,
> And to remember his holy covenant,
> The oath which he swore to Abraham our father,
> To grant us that, being delivered out of the hand of our enemies,
> We should serve him without fear,
> In holiness and righteousness before him all our days."

Clement's head was swimming as he made his way to the street. *Such a confusing set of contradictions!* he thought. *These men say that salvation is so easy that a single step is all that is needed. Then they say that this step is the most difficult step one can take. On the one hand, they deny superiority to others, and then they speak as if God himself belonged only to them. Everybody else who tries to be somebody actually becomes nobody, but these nobodies who repent actually succeed in becoming somebody. It doesn't make any difference whether a person is Jew or Gentile, rich or poor—he is lost unless he accepts this Jesus as his Master. But if he does accept Jesus, then it matters even less what race or class he belongs to. Then these disciples say that one can't hope to understand all these contradictions unless one believes in Jesus. But if one believes, then one will understand them.*

As Clement tussled with these puzzles, his inner turmoil

increased. He tried savagely to blot the whole affair out of his mind. *If only I could forget that these people ever existed,* he thought. But the more he tried, the more he failed. And he didn't know whether to be more irritated with himself or with them. He was even farther from happiness than ever. If only he could be as sure of things as Julian, or his father, or even Marcus! Instead, he seemed miserably uncertain of everything.

CHAPTER 12

Herald of War

Boys," said Sabinus the next morning when he came around to inspect their progress, "I have news for you. Let me warn you to watch your step the next few days. Anything can happen when the furies are loose."

"What's up?" inquired Julian.

"Tigellinus is about to locate the guilt for the fire. The secret police have been combing the streets to find the culprits, but so far they have failed. Now they have stumbled across the rumors that hold Nero responsible. You can imagine the emperor's fury. He has ordered Tigellinus to find a group already in public disfavor on whom the blame can be shifted. Tigellinus has gone to work. He is drawing his net on the scapegoats, and he's sure to catch many innocent people. Nero has announced a great spectacle for tomorrow night. He plans to make known the criminals and to give people a chance to watch their punishment.

"Clement, it is your people who are in greatest danger—I think it would be wise for you to warn them, if they value their lives, to keep off the streets, to avoid all meetings, and to be prepared for anything. No one knows where the lightning will strike."

Thanking Sabinus and putting away his tools, Clement hastened back to Bar-Joseph's home. He would have run had he not been afraid of creating undue suspicion. As he walked through the business and governmental districts, he noted extra contingents of police patrolling the streets and stationed at the gates. Filled with foreboding, he climbed the steps to Bar-Joseph's home.

Bar-Joseph received the news as if he had long expected it. He was grateful, however, for the warning and immediately laid plans to meet the emergency. Elders in each of the fifteen synagogues must be warned quietly, for any excitement might only precipitate mob action. Particularly vulnerable were those outstanding leaders who had alienated the authorities on earlier occasions. Since they might be singled out for special arrest, they must be advised to leave the city for a time. Mob action too must be anticipated. Any home or synagogue might be the target for vandals, inflamed by personal hatred, by business grudges, or by the charges of the politicians.

The elder quickly wrote notes to the key leaders. He gave ten of them to Clement, an equal number to another messenger, and dispatched them with careful instructions. It was Clement's first exploration into some sections of the city, but he found their homes without much trouble and delivered the letters. By early afternoon the work was done, and the Jewish community was gathering its resources for the crisis.

While on his various errands, Clement kept turning and returning in his mind to the little group at the house of Jonas. Undoubtedly they lay in unusual jeopardy. Several of them were already in prison. They did not have the support and influence of any long-established synagogue. Many of the disciples were recent immigrants. Their cult had not been recognized as legal, and the Jewish community would not accept responsibility for them. Clement recalled the Jew in the Forum who had angrily protested that Peter was not speaking for the Jews. He remembered too the sharp heckling that Peter had received from Gentiles. He recalled the feeling of guilt at his own refusal to acknowledge his faith in Peter's God, when the arrest was being made. Had he done so, he thought with a start, he might now be in jail with the apostle. If so, his life would be worth very little. There came back to him certain things that Marcus had said last night: "Every disciple must take up his cross—" "Unless a man renounces everything he owns—" Yes, these believers were undoubtedly realistic about the price of their faith.

Clement suddenly realized that he had still another duty to complete: he must warn Jonas as he had warned the others. He finished his last errand for Bar-Joseph, and then, without telling anyone of his own errand, he hurried down the Appian Way. The afternoon was almost gone when he knocked at the familiar door.

Jonas greeted him. "May peace be yours!" Clement told him the news, and, in telling it, realized that he himself was more apprehensive over the fate of this group than he was about the synagogues.

"I am not surprised," replied Jonas calmly. "We have been taught to expect this. Our Master knew what we would face, and his experience has been ours wherever we have lived. Moreover, Marcus was not permitted to visit

Peter today. One of the sentries who had earlier been kind to us warned Marcus, if he valued his life, to stay away for several days."

"You will warn the disciples?" asked Clement.

"Yes, I shall send a messenger to the various homes. But every true follower of Christ has settled this issue in advance. We have already faced a worse crisis than this," Jonas continued, speaking more to himself than to Clement. "For us the sole issue is whether we shall be loyal to God or to men, whether we shall follow the Messiah and despise the world's hatred or betray the Messiah in our fear of the world."

Suddenly Jonas remembered Clement. He remembered too that he was not a believer, and recognized the risk he had taken in behalf of the Christians. "We are very grateful to you," he added warmly. "You are more of a disciple than you think. Won't you stay to worship with us tonight?"

"Do you mean that you will hold the meeting in spite of the danger?" asked Clement, incredulous.

"Not in spite of the danger, but because of it. Of course I am alarmed. All of us will be. We don't want to die, and this danger will tempt us to choose the easier road. But we know that we can resist temptation best when we are gathered together, praying and singing in the name of the Crucified One, and relying upon his strength."

Clement was impressed by this calm reasoning, but he hastened to reply: "No, I can't stay. I may be needed at home." *Is that the reason,* he thought guiltily, *or am I afraid of being associated with this group just now?* Jonas did not press the invitation. Thanking Clement again, he bade him farewell. "The Lord watch over you."

As Clement hurried back to the Janiculan hill, it occurred to him that he knew now the answer to his father's question. These people did not reject the Law because they wanted an easier path of compromise with the world. They might be foolish, but they were no cowards.

The evening at Bar-Joseph's was one to test their courage. At any moment fury might strike. Consequently each moment seemed like an hour. The house was crowded. In addition to the family and guests, a number of the elders had gathered in order to plan how to meet any emergency that might develop. Bar-Joseph led the assembly in evening prayers, and then they waited.

The house was dark, and the streets in the Jewish section were practically deserted. Once during the evening a messenger brought reassuring news. Poppaea, the emperor's wife, was said to be interceding in behalf of the Jews. She had occasionally attended the Synagogue of the Asians, whether out of curiosity, superstitious fear, or inner conviction, no one could tell. Now she was exerting a friendly influence at the court, having talked that day with both Tigellinus and the emperor. There was, of course, some danger in her support. Loyal Romans detested Poppaea, and for her to betray the Roman deities by flirting with Oriental cults meant that some patriots were likely to take revenge, not on Poppaea, who was beyond the reach of their violence, but on the cults she favored. Nero too had dabbled in foreign religions. He had been initiated into Mithraism, and for a time had been intrigued by the worship of the Syrian goddess. His disloyalty to Roman customs, however, was taken for granted.

Still later another courier appeared with a suggestion for avoiding the impending danger. "We shall be safe," he urged, "if we can deflect the blow toward the followers of Jesus. Let us send a committee of our most respected leaders to inform Tigellinus that we are not responsible and to turn over to him a list of Christians who should be investigated."

To this suggestion Bar-Joseph gave a vigorous rejoinder. "Should we try to escape by accusing other innocent people? Have you forgotten that these men are also sons of Abraham, who worship the God of Abraham? While we do not accept their Messiah, we have nothing to fear from them as a group, certainly not as compared with the blasphemies of the pagans. And, however much we dislike them, we know that they are not guilty of setting fire to Rome. We should be no better than Nero if we too were responsible for the shedding of innocent blood."

Some of the elders were inclined to argue the point, but, much to Clement's relief, Bar-Joseph's authority carried sufficient weight. Clement's thoughts flew to Peter and Jonas and Della. These people were Christians because they were first Jews, because they believed—however true or false—that God had kept his promise to Israel. He felt the stab of an uneasy conscience. *If I were as brave as they, would I have stayed at the house of Jonas for the meeting? Or do I belong among those who would crucify Jesus? Or shall I always try to remain neutral?* He wondered what was happening now in Jonas' home, and whether the police had interrupted the meeting yet.

At the home of Jonas there had been, in fact, little to distinguish this evening from the others. The believers had gathered at the usual time and in the usual numbers. There were fewer inquirers in the back seats, but their absence made little difference to the disciples. Marcus did not appear. After the unsuccessful attempt to visit the prisoners, he had spent the afternoon in carrying gifts and cheer to the prisoners' families. Since he had not appeared in time for the meeting there was an undercurrent of deep concern about him. No one knew whether he had been arrested or had merely found an urgent errand to another of the house Churches. In his absence Jonas took his place as leader. He selected one of the psalms to read. Everyone present knew the reason for his choice, for within each person the battle was being waged between fear and faith.

"'My God, my God, why hast thou forsaken me? Why art thou so far from helping me? O my God, I cry in the daytime, but thou hearest not; and in the night season, and am not silent. But thou art holy, O thou that inhabitest the praises of Israel. Our fathers trusted in thee: they trusted and thou didst deliver them. They cried unto thee and were delivered: they trusted in thee, and were not confounded. But I am a worm, and no man; a reproach of men, and despised of the people. All they that see me laugh me to scorn: they shoot out the lip, they shake the head, saying, He trusted on the Lord that he would deliver him; let him deliver him, seeing he delighted in him. I am poured out like water, and all my bones are out of joint: my heart is like wax; it is melted in the midst of my bowels. My strength is dried up like a potsherd; and my tongue cleaveth to my jaws; and thou hast brought me into the dust of death. For dogs have compassed me: the assembly of the wicked have inclosed me; they pierced my hands and my feet. I may count all my bones. They look and stare upon me: they part my garments among them, and cast lots for my clothing.
"'But be not thou far from me, O Lord: O my strength, hasten to help me. Deliver my soul from the sword. Save me from the lion's mouth. I will declare thy name unto my brethren: in the midst of the congregation will I praise thee. Ye that fear the Lord, praise him; all ye sons of Jacob, glorify him. For he hath not despised nor abhorred the affliction of the afflicted; neither hath he hid his face from him; but when he cried unto him, he heard. All the ends of the world shall remember and turn unto the Lord; and all the kindreds of the nations shall worship before thee. For the kingdom is the Lord's; and he is the governor among the nations.'

"Let us remember the suffering of our Lord," continued Jonas after he had finished reading. "When he was crucified, he cried out with the words of this psalm: 'My God, my God, why hast thou forsaken me?' And God heard him, and delivered him. Our Lord trusted God, and he was not put to shame.

"On the night in which he was betrayed, Jesus went unto the Mount of Olives with his disciples. He said to them, 'Sit here, while I pray.' And he took with him Peter, James, and John, and began to be troubled. He said to them, 'My soul is very sorrowful, even to death; remain here, and watch.' And going a little farther, he fell on the ground and prayed that, if it were possible, the hour might pass from him. 'Father, all things are possible to thee; remove this cup from me; yet not what I will, but what thou wilt.' When he came back he found them sleeping. He said to Peter: 'What, are you asleep? Could you not watch one hour? Watch and pray that you may not enter into temptation.'

"Jesus knew that his followers would be called to face the same crises he faced. To prepare them, he had warned them:

"'They will deliver you up to courts; you will be beaten in synagogues; you will stand before governors and kings for my sake to bear testimony before them. When they bring you to trial, do not be anxious beforehand about what you shall say; say whatever is given you to say in that hour, for it is not you, but the Holy Spirit who will speak. Brother will deliver up brother to death, the father his child, and children their parents. You will be hated by all for my name's sake. But whoever endures to the end will be saved.'

Let us be grateful for this reward which he has promised:

"'Blessed are you poor, for yours is the kingdom of God. Blessed are you who are hungry now, for you shall be satisfied.

Blessed are you who weep now, for you shall laugh.
Blessed are you when men hate you, and reject your
    name as evil,
        On account of the Son of man!
Rejoice in that day, and leap for joy,
For your reward is great in heaven;
For so their fathers treated the prophets.'

"We are afraid. Yet we are prepared. Should we be arrested or even executed, we know how to treat the soldiers—as Jesus treated those who killed him. 'Do not return
evil for evil or reviling for reviling; but on the contrary
bless, for to this you have been called, that you may obtain a blessing. Have no fear of them, nor be troubled, but
in your hearts reverence Christ as Lord. Always be prepared to make a defense to any one who calls you to account for the hope that is in you, yet do it with gentleness
and reverence; and keep your conscience clear, so that,
when you are abused, those who revile your good behavior
in Christ may be put to shame.' "

There was no disposition that evening to argue or to discuss Jonas' counsel. The believers had heard these commands many times before, but never had they seemed so
difficult or so compelling. Some could not keep from
watching the door. And indeed, before Jonas had finished,
the expected intrusion came. The door burst open, and
there were the police. One of the women screamed; several
disciples shifted nervously in their seats. Then there was
nothing but tense silence.

The captain looked at his list. "Is there a man here by
the name of Jonas?"

"I am Jonas." The leader paused a moment and then
went on, "We have done nothing wrong, but if you must
arrest someone, take me and let the rest go."

"Hold your tongue," was the harsh reply. Two soldiers

with swords in hand walked to Jonas and escorted him to the door.

Consulting his list again, the captain called out, "Andronicus."

Without comment, this disciple stood up and walked to the door.

"Marcus."

"He is not here," replied Jonas.

"Where is he?"

"None of us knows. We supposed that you had already taken him." The captain nodded to two soldiers to search the house.

"And which is Epaenetus?"

"Here I am," replied that brother reluctantly. He kissed his wife, and walked slowly to the door, shaking with fear.

"Hermes."

Hermes broke under the strain and almost shouted at the officer: "Sir, you have made a mistake. I don't belong to this group. I am only a visitor. I am loyal to Caesar."

"Hold your tongue too. You can do your explaining at headquarters."

"Mary."

"I am Mary, sir," came the timid but steady response. Andronicus interrupted, addressing the officer: "Must you take women too? Surely you know that they are innocent. Do what you want with us men, but don't harm them."

"It's all right, Andronicus," came the clear voice of Mary. "I am ready to go, grateful that the Lord has called me to give my testimony."

The captain continued the roll call, as if he had not heard. "Julia."

Julia went to the door quickly to stand with her husband, Epaenetus.

"Those are all the names I have," the captain concluded.

"I ought to arrest all of you, but I warn you that I may be back. If the rest of you are wise, you will get out of Rome tonight and stay out."

"Peace be with you," spoke one of those who were left. "We shall be praying for you. You soldiers are fighting against the Lord of heaven and earth."

Della addressed her farewell to the brothers and to her husband: "May our Christ strengthen you and give you peace."

The Peace of the Cross

THE next day found Julian and Clement at work as usual. Julian was visibly relieved to see Clement, and he rapidly drew from him the story of his activities as a messenger of warning the day before. Clement also told Julian of the placard he had seen posted that very morning.

"Attention, loyal Romans," it had read. "You are invited to a spectacle in Nero's Circus this evening. In addition to the games, the emperor will make an extraordinary address on the state of the nation. Justice will be administered to certain enemies of the state, found guilty of hideous crimes. There will be refreshments for all."

"They got someone," was Julian's response.

"I'm thankful they didn't raid our quarters," said Clement. "Things seemed unusually quiet across the Tiber." How had the Christians fared, he wondered uneasily.

When Sabinus came to inspect the work, he saw that the boys were hungry for news. "The police are not telling who were arrested," he said. "Tigellinus and his crew of murderers were busy all night, but I haven't been able to learn who fell into their net. Someone told me that the raids were transferred from the synagogues to the followers of Jesus. But no one knows how many are being held. It's almost certain death for them."

Clement shuddered and turned pale. This word shocked him more deeply than he had supposed it would. But he tried to hide his alarm. Sabinus, noticing his nervousness, misinterpreted it.

"Wouldn't you be safer to stay here on the Esquiline tonight?" he asked gently. "The danger is not yet over; the mobs may get loose tonight. You would be safe here, and you're welcome to stay."

Clement was grateful for this courtesy, but declined as graciously as he could. "My place is with my people," he said. After Sabinus had left, Clement thought: *Yes, my place is with my people. But who are my people? That part of Israel which is more safe, or that part which is in greatest danger?* Stories flooded his mind from the reservoir of his memory—stories of the heroes of his people: Moses, Joseph, Elijah, Jeremiah, Daniel, Esther, Mattathias and his five sons. In every case, he recalled, there had been a sharp contrast between the majority who had saved their lives by conforming to an alien world and the minority who risked death in unflinching loyalty to God. Would another chapter be added to that story tonight?

Not much work was accomplished that day, for there was too much excitement everywhere. Many looked upon the day as a holiday, with the special celebration promised as its climax. Others were caught up in the blanket of mystery, suspicion and dread. They fed on rumors and seemed to delight in starting more of them. They predicted who would be caught and how punishment would be executed. And these guesses, carried about on the wings of whispers, grew into semiofficial or official announcements.

But no one trusted any reports, however authoritative they seemed to be. No one actually knew the answers to the questions of the day: who had been arrested, how they would be punished, where the reprisals would stop, and how great was the danger of civil war.

Julian debated with himself whether to attend the mass celebration, his craving for information competing with his distaste for exhibitions of cruelty. The knowledge of Nero's blood lust made him hesitate. However, this would be an excellent chance to keep in touch with developments, and to gauge for himself the loyalty of the people to the emperor. Lentulus was eager to go, and finally Julian agreed to accompany him. "Perhaps," he told Clement "I can do your people a good turn by reporting the proceedings."

Neither the lure of the crowd nor the lust for excitement tempted Clement. For, if any of his people were there, they would be found in the arena rather than in the gallery. And his place belonged among his own kinsfolk. But, again, who were his real family? Should he go to join those in the house of Bar-Joseph or those in the house of Jonas? Which lay in greater peril? So far the Synagogue of the Olive Tree had been untouched. Was that true of Jonas' company? They had planned to meet last night in spite of his warning. What had happened? Should he have stayed with them? Had some or all of them been arrested? This time he did not take long to decide. His greater anxiety was for the Christians, and he determined to learn their fate as soon as work was done.

It was not Jonas who welcomed Clement that evening with his gracious, "Peace be with you." Instead, it was

Jonas' wife. Her face was strained, but her welcome was no less genuine than her husband's had been. The others too greeted him with cordiality. The word had spread that it was Clement who had come to warn them on the previous evening, and they now treated him more as a disciple than as an inquirer.

It was not hard for Clement to see how much damage had been done to the little Christian fellowship by the arrests. He could recall the faces of those who were missing, and he did not need to ask the reason for their absence. He was more than ever amazed by the quiet fortitude with which these folk took their stand against the world. Their faces showed the strain of personal fear and of anxiety for loved ones who had been imprisoned; at the same time they showed a sober determination to accept whatever calamity might strike. They had placed all earthly hopes on one side of the balance, and had discovered another hope on the other side that outweighed everything else. And this single strong hope produced a gratitude that kept them free of hysteria. Almost every disciple was present except those who had been jailed, but Clement seemed to be the only one of the inquirers who had risked arrest to come to worship with them.

The Scripture chosen for the evening was the Second Psalm. It was read slowly but clearly by Silvanus, who accepted without comment the post left vacant by Marcus and Jonas:

" 'Why do the nations rage,
  And the peoples plot in vain?
  The kings of the earth take their stand,
  And the rulers take counsel together,
  Against the Lord, and against his anointed, saying,
  Let us break their bonds asunder,
  And cast away their cords from us.
  He who sits in the heavens will laugh:

The Lord will have them in derision.
Then will he speak to them in his wrath,
And vex them in his sore displeasure:
Yet I have appointed my own king
On my holy hill of Zion.
I will tell of his decree:
The Lord said unto me, Thou art my son;
This day have I begotten thee.
Ask of me, and I will make the nations your inheritance,
And all parts of the earth your possession.
Thou shalt break them with a rod of iron;
Thou shalt dash them in pieces like pottery.
Now therefore be wise, O kings:
Be instructed, ye judges of the earth.
Serve the Lord with fear,
Lest he be angry, and you perish in the way,
For his wrath will soon be kindled.
Blessed are all who take refuge in him.' "

The worshipers knew which nations and kings were fighting against God. They did not need Silvanus to tell them who the King was whom God had anointed. Silvanus merely reminded them of what they knew.

"Of whom was David speaking in this psalm I have just read if not of God's Anointed? And whom has God anointed if not his Son of whom he said: "Thou art my son; this day have I begotten thee? And what other king have we, if not this King whom God has placed upon the holy hill of Zion? And with what baptism did God baptize him, if not the baptism of suffering, rejection by the world? And how was this Son made perfect, if not by his obedience unto death? And whom did this Son glorify, if not the Father who had chosen him?

" 'If any man comes to me and hates not his own father and mother and wife and children and brothers and sisters, yes, and his own life also, he cannot be my disciple. Whoever does not bear his own cross and come after me, cannot be my disciple.'

"If we then are called upon to suffer for the sake of the Messiah, it is the sign of our sonship and a sign that already the final conflict between our King and all the kings of the earth is upon us.

"The psalmist makes clear to us the two choices that are ours," continued Silvanus. "We may choose to fear Nero, the king of the earth, because of his power to destroy our bodies. Or we may choose to fear God our Lord, who has power to destroy both body and soul. And if we choose God, we will be ready to follow his Son, however the king of the earth may rage."

This clear, sharp description of the situation made Clement stir uneasily. He knew that Silvanus and the disciples had forgotten that he was present, in their preoccupation with their own problem. They were trying to concentrate all their attention upon their vision of a Master who offered in one hand death and in the other life. But the decisiveness with which they faced their choice made it difficult for Clement to evade the same choice.

Was Jesus the Son whom God had chosen as King above all kings? Clement wondered. Either he was or he was not. If he was not, then Satan had indeed deluded these people, had used a strange lure to lead them down a road of useless suffering to their own destruction. On the other hand, if Jesus was actually God's anointed King, then these hunted disciples were right in standing against the whole world, and their courage was a sign that God was on their side.

How could a man be expected to decide which of these alternatives was true? No one could judge by external proofs. Those who killed seemed as confident of God's approval as those who were killed. Yet the issue was so sharp that it was impossible to remain neutral, to postpone decision until events would show which was stronger—Nero or Jesus.

Yet Clement was not ready to decide. In his struggle, he breathed a prayer: "O God, forgive me for my ignorance, for my weakness, for my confusion. I do not know which way to turn. But whichever be thy true purpose for me, give me power to obey."

As he prayed, there came into his torn mind a healing word: "I have forgiven you. Fear not." And an image flashed across the screen of his mind's eye—a man hanging upon a cross. What made him think of that? Was it a product of his fearful imagination as he pictured the events that now might be taking place in the Circus? Or was it transferred to his mind from the words of Silvanus? Silvanus was still speaking:

". . . It was as he faced death that our Master learned what obedience means. Like us, he prayed that the cup might be taken from him. And his Father answered his prayer, not by snatching him away from the men who crucified him, but by giving him the power of perfect obedience. God has sent him for this very purpose—to forgive us our cowardice and to give us power to obey him even in death."

These words, coming as a response to his own prayer, made Clement's burden seem as light as feathers, as if at last the decision had been taken off his own shoulders. His prayer had been answered. At the deepest point of confusion and weakness, he had been forgiven. And the forgiveness banished his fear and despair. He had asked for power to obey, and the Man on the cross had shown the way. Here was the power he needed. What a relief from all the nagging questions, from all the hesitations of a mind fighting against itself! Clement yielded himself, and found his heart expand with joyful assurance.

He was, of course, too overwhelmed by freedom and joy to be able or to want to put the experience into words. At a level far below the surface of speech, his heart knew that, in Jesus, God had forgiven him—that Jesus had now become actually the Messiah for him and that he, Clement, now actually belonged to this new Master.

He was dimly aware that many questions remained unanswered. He didn't yet know all the steps that would follow. But he was sure of this first one, and sure that his new Lord would take care of the other matters when the time came. And these brothers would help him too. For now they actually were his brothers. He listened with new understanding to what Silvanus was saying.

". . . We confess to one another how frightened we are, how tempted we are to deny the Lord who died for us. But we remind one another of his words:

> "'A disciple is not above his teacher;
> A servant is not above his Lord;
> It is enough for the disciple to imitate his teacher
> And for the servant to imitate his Lord.'

As we strive to follow our Lord, he gives us a place in his Kingdom. He shares with us his cup of suffering and joy. And this cup makes us brothers. When we say, 'Jesus is Lord,' we become one body, the Body of Christ. And through us, he wins his triumph over all his adversaries. In this hour of need, let us pray to our common Lord, knowing that he will give us his peace."

As the Christians bowed in prayer, and began their confession, "Jesus is Lord," Clement felt his heart being welded into the chain of fellowship. Words spontaneously shaped themselves in his mind. Then they were on his lips: "Jesus is Lord. Lord, make me worthy to be one of thy servants." And deep in his heart, he heard the answer: "Thou too art my son. And these are your brothers."

To this assurance he responded without reservation. All the bars of inner resistance had collapsed. He felt the tug of Christ drawing him into the circle of peace and joy. He forgot himself completely in the marvel of God's presence; into the opened gates of his spirit rushed a wave of gratitude, and he murmured, "I thank thee, God"; but he gave no external sign of the power that had so silently worked its miracle within him.

The prayers of the company soon turned into a hymn with which they were familiar:

"Who shall separate us from the love of Christ?
Shall tribulation, or anguish, or persecution,
Or famine, or nakedness, or the sword?
No, in all these things we are more than conquerors
    through him who loved us.
Neither death, nor life, nor angels, nor powers,
Nor things present, nor things to come, nor height nor
    depth,
Shall be able to separate us from the love of God
Which is in Christ Jesus our Lord."

When the final amens had been given, Clement hardly knew what to do. He was suddenly embarrassed by the necessity for talking with these believers, yet he could not slip out as he had done on previous occasions. He waited at the door until Silvanus was free, and then awkwardly asked if he might be included within the fellowship.

Silvanus, wise and understanding, did not reply at once, but looked long and deeply into Clement's eyes to make certain that his decision had not been hastily or unknowingly arrived at.

"You know what such a step means?"

"Yes."

"And you are sure that God has called you into this fellowship?"

"Yes. I tried hard to escape him, but every way was barred against me, and I am certain now that he has won."

Silvanus led Clement into the adjoining room where the table was spread for supper. There he told the others of Clement's decision. They welcomed him with warm friendliness, but it was easy to see that their thoughts were directed, not toward Clement, but toward the absent ones, and the trials which perhaps awaited them all.

When they were ready to begin eating, Silvanus gave the blessing of the food, and added some words that were strange to Clement, but very dear to the others:

"In the night when he was betrayed the Lord Jesus took bread, and gave thanks for it. Then he broke it, saying: 'This is my body, broken for you. When you eat it, remember me.'"

They ate the meal soberly and in silence—a silence alive with memories and hopes. Near the end Silvanus pronounced a blessing over the wine, and added:

"In that same night, after the supper, Jesus took the cup, saying: 'This cup is the new covenant in my blood. When you drink it, remember me. As often as you eat this bread and drink this cup, you proclaim the Lord's death until he comes.'"

When all had finished, they stood together and sang a doxology:

"Unto him who loved us and freed us from our sins by his
    blood,
Who made us to be a kingdom, to be priests unto his
    God and Father,
To him be the glory and the dominion for ever and ever.
    Amen."

Then Silvanus dismissed them with the assurance:

"'The God of all grace, who called you to his eternal glory in Christ, after that we have suffered a little while, shall himself perfect, establish, strengthen you. To him be the dominion for ever and ever. Amen.'"

CHAPTER 14

A First Confession

JULIAN found it hard to wait until Clement came to work the next morning. For Julian had attended Nero's spectacle. He had heard the announcement of the charges made against the criminals, and had seen their punishment. So when Clement appeared for work, Julian immediately began the ghastly tale. The story was necessarily interrupted by the requirements of their work on the building; but on this occasion their progress on the wall was actually very slow. They were too much absorbed in the story even to think about their employer or their reputations as masons.

First Julian pictured the amphitheater filled with Romans of all classes. Never had the emperor and his retinue staged a more lavish show. The imperial boxes were filled with Nero's admirers and associates, all bent on making this a gala occasion. The senators occupied boxes reserved

159

for them, though probably fear of displeasing the dictator was for most of them the reason for being present. The Imperial Guard, the police, and city officials appeared in their most imposing uniforms, marching in impressive phalanxes. It was obvious that Nero intended this demonstration as a warning to all malcontents. Thousands upon thousands of the common people had swarmed together—out to make the most of a free show. Julian, who had been accustomed only to the more restrained assemblies of a small town, was quite carried away by the size of the crowd and by the magnificence of the occasion. He had never witnessed such power concentrated in one small enclosure. Particularly was he amazed at the popularity of the emperor. When the royal party staged its entrance, the throng stood at attention and cheered wildly for many minutes. True, Julian heard and felt among the onlookers an undercurrent of resentment and subdued sarcasm, but the prospect of food and a fight, the dramatic display of imperial power, the contagion of numbers, and the fear of being observed by plain-clothes police—all these effectively submerged latent antagonisms.

The curtain raiser was a gladiatorial combat between two of Rome's most popular fighters. As this combat reached its brutal end, the onlookers were caught up in a bedlam of excitement and cheering. Awaiting eagerly the verdict of the emperor, the crowd were both astonished and pleased to see him spare the life of the gallant gladiator who had been defeated.

Then, in a voice which had been carefully trained for the stage, the emperor made his announcement. Julian mimicked his pompous, stentorian tone:

"Loyal Romans," he began, "in July our beloved city underwent the worst catastrophe in its history. From that disaster we have all suffered. Priceless treasures from Roman history were lost. My own palace was destroyed. And many of you lost your shops and your homes. Many of you grieve for members of your families, and there is none among us who does not mourn the loss of friends. Blessed be their memory. But though we have been saddened by these losses, the Roman spirit has not been defeated.

"Together we have worked to rebuild our city. Your Government has moved with lightning speed to meet your needs. We have fed and housed the homeless. We have rushed in relief supplies. We have kept the price of corn low. We have provided work for all who want it. As a result, we can now hope for steady progress in security and health. More than that, we can have confidence that the new Rome which is emerging will surpass in dignity and beauty anything in the past. To this end, your emperor has devoted his time, his thought, his money. To this end, the temples have gladly contributed from their treasuries. To this end, merchants and knights and senators have made huge donations. To this end, the provinces have sent in their tribute to the Eternal City. You too have worked in rebuilding homes and shops and roads. United by common loyalties to the gods and to our fathers, we have met heroically the greatest crisis facing our generation.

"But one thing has been lacking—the discovery and arrest of those enemies of Rome who were responsible for the fire, those wretches who sought to destroy our beloved city. Night and day, our faithful police have been tracking down these despicable culprits, for whom no fate can be terrible enough to repay their treachery. At last, Tigellinus and his noble defenders of law and order have rounded up the criminals. Today in your sight they will receive justice, the justice of an empire which they have desecrated. And you will have a part in giving them their just dues. Let me now present the faithful Tigellinus who caught the criminals and who will read you the record of their guilt."

The official received a huge ovation. After the shouting had ceased, he made his elaborate tribute to Nero, and then proceeded to read the indictment:

"Be it known unto you, divine emperor, that we have found men guilty of the following crimes:

"In the first place, they have refused to worship our gods, and have blasphemously denied that they exist. They refuse to propitiate our historic deities, and spurn the rites of allegiance which we as Romans owe to the protectors of the state. They flout our temples, and proclaim the imminent destruction of all our temples and our gods.

"In the second place, they are completely crazed by magic and superstition. All the world, they claim, is soon to be destroyed by fire, and the fire of this judgment is to begin in Rome. The fire which devastated parts of our fair city was, they say, only the beginning of other and greater conflagrations. All who do not believe as they do are to be destroyed. We have heard them shouting this threat even in the Forum itself.

"In the third place, this group meets regularly and illegally. No license has ever been granted them. They gather secretly in homes hidden away in the worst sections of the slums. Their members come from the lowest level of the population—ignorant, poverty-stricken, and obscure foreigners who have always been a threat to the fair name of our city.

"In the fourth place, they practice, in their secret meetings, all sorts of vicious crimes against humanity, such as drinking human blood, and plotting the overthrow of all existing kingdoms. We have given them freedom, but they have used this freedom to plot our downfall. They follow one whom they call king, but this king of theirs is a criminal from Galilee, whom our procurator, Pontius Pilate, executed years ago on charges of sedition and high treason. They are called after this leader—Christians. And they freely confess and stubbornly refuse to change their faith. I present them to you, noble emperor and loyal Romans, as guilty of setting fire to our city, guilty of treason to our gods and to our emperor, and guilty of hatred toward the whole human race. I recommend the most hideous punishment that lies in your power."

The whole stadium burst into vindictive applause—cheering, shouting, cursing. "Long live the emperor!" "Death to our enemies!" As soon as the noise subsided, the emperor gave the signal for the penalties to be inflicted.

Across one end of the arena a row of crosses had been erected. One by one the soldiers had led in a group of men and had slowly nailed them to the wood. The spikes had been driven first through the hands and then through the feet; all the while the mob howled in derision. Some had been hung head downward, and the soldiers, goaded by the crowd, had mutilated the bodies in order to increase the writhing.

Then, in full view of the crosses, other Christians had been thrown into the arena, wrapped in hides of wild beasts, the skins still dripping with the blood of the animals. Gates had been opened to a pack of hungry hunting dogs, howling at the smell of blood. It had not taken them long to complete their grisly work. When the crowd had become satiated by these sights, the emperor announced that food would be served in the gardens and that the worst of the criminals would be punished there.

Nero had led the way in his chariot; then came a procession of state officials. The crowd had followed, stam-

peding through the gates to see what new tortures had
been devised. On each side of the gardens were stakes to
which men and women had been bound naked, their
bodies black with pitch. At a signal from Tigellinus, soldiers had lighted the fires, turning the victims into torches
that blazed and smoked while food was being served to
onlookers, and men joked and shuddered at the fiendish
torture.

Julian finished his recital in a low voice. He had been so
shocked and horrified by the whole spectacle that sleep
that night had been impossible for him. "Only a fool would
believe that these people were responsible for the fire," he
added. "Incendiaries don't work in such numbers, nor do
they confess guilt so readily. What was almost incredible
to me was the quiet and calmness of the victims. None of
them seemed to fear death. None of them showed anger
against their tormentors. In fact, their faces were alight
with confident belief, as though this occasion was a means
of fulfilling a purpose of their own. Some of us felt that
they should have been in the role of judges, trying those
who had condemned them. A strange justice indeed! No
wonder that Seneca despaired of influencing this brutal
emperor, and finally gave up his political career."

Julian had been so absorbed in his story—it would be a
long time before he could free his mind of the whole
hideous spectacle—that he hardly noticed Clement's reaction to his telling of it. So he was unprepared for the tale
that Clement began now to tell, the story of what had
happened to him while Julian was at the Circus. Julian's
obvious disgust with the events he had witnessed made it
easier for Clement to release to his friend something of the
inner revolution he had undergone. For all the while that
Julian had been picturing the lurid scenes in the Circus,
Clement had been setting over against them the sober

meeting in the house of Jonas. When Julian had been echo-
ing the cries of the bloodthirsty mob, Clement's ears had
heard again the hymns of the persecuted.

"I am not surprised," he began slowly, "that these who
were butchered and burned showed such courage and confidence. Last night, when Nero was gloating over their
agony, I was in the home of one who probably was a vic-
tim. I had supper with those who love what Nero hates.
They sang one of their hymns. It goes like this:

"Neither death, nor life, nor angels, nor powers,
  Nor things present, nor things to come, nor height, nor
    depth,
  Shall be able to separate us from the love of God
  Which is in Christ Jesus our Lord.

All the police in the world are powerless before such
faith."

Julian was dumfounded. "You mean to say that you
risked your life by going there even after Sabinus' warning?"

"Yes, I did. And furthermore, I share their belief. I too
am now a Christian."

"A Christian? You?" Julian was speechless with amaze-
ment and concern for his friend.

"Yes, I became one last night. Or rather, I have begun
to follow Christ. I hope someday to be a worthy bearer of
the name. I sang that hymn last night too, and as I sang it
I knew beyond any doubt that it is true."

Clement felt immense relief at having made his first
confession. He felt somehow that another step had been
taken along the road that Jonas and Simon Peter and Jesus
had walked. There was now no going back, no chance of
waking up to find that he had been dreaming. This declaration, even to a good friend, was a stone cemented

firmly into the structure of his new faith. His freedom from fear in making it also made him aware that a new strength had entered his will, like nothing he had ever felt.

"What you said about the victor and his victims was absolutely true," he continued. "They alone have won the right to judge the world. Nero and his people actually condemn themselves. The disciples of Jesus are wise, and their persecutors are senseless. They are alive, and their tormentors are dead. I would rather share their life and die as they die than be found in Nero's company in life or in death."

"Not so loud," warned Julian, as Lentulus approached.

"Has Julian been telling you what happened last night?" asked Lentulus.

"Yes, he told me the whole story. It was about what I had expected."

Julian and Clement busied themselves at the wall until Lentulus, finding no market for his gossip, went back to his work.

At the next opportunity Clement continued. "Sooner or later one has to take sides in this matter as I have had to. It isn't possible for a man to remain neutral. He must stand either with Nero or with Jesus and his followers. Why don't you come with me after work, Julian, and visit a meeting of the disciples? It might help you if you saw how these Christians stand today, after last night's butchery."

"Don't hurry me," was Julian's reply. "I can't take much more in one day."

Respecting their mutual need for silence, Clement and Julian worked the rest of the day, fitting stones into the building and fitting patterns of thought into new niches. And the supply of both was ample.

Clement's thoughts began with the image of Nero and the scenes in the stadium. But these pictures faded out

into others. He visualized Pilate and that earlier Crucifixion, then Antiochus Epiphanes and the fate of Mattathias
and his five sons, then Belshazzar, and Nebuchadnezzar,
and the Pharaohs, then Pilate again. All epochs of history
seemed to mix themselves together in his mind.

Yes, he thought, *we should in a way be grateful to these
tyrants, for God somehow uses their very bestiality to
make plain the choice that men face. We might never be
forced to decide for God unless in someone like Nero we
were able to see what results when men decide against
God.*

A little later Clement asked Julian whether he had remembered any of the Christians' names. Julian recalled
that Tigellinus had spoken of several in the garden, but
he had recognized only one—Peter.

"Did you hear the name of Jonas?" asked Clement with
deep misgivings.

Julian hesitated. "The names were all strange to me and
I can't be sure. But I think that was one of them."

Clement shuddered, certain in his own mind that the
gentle, gracious Jonas had been executed. He shuddered
too in the realization that had he accepted Jonas' invitation to stay with the Christians on that earlier night, he
might well have been executed by the side of Jonas. *And
if Jonas is dead, so are all the others from his house who
were arrested.*

So this is the issue, he thought. *Do I choose to stand
with Nero who is alive or with Peter who is dead? A part
of me shudders at the thought of dying with Peter. But
another part would be proud of that death. The first self
shouts at the other, "You fool!"—and the second half shouts
back, "You coward!"*

*The problem is one of which self I really am. As far back
as I can remember, my mind has been divided, one self*

battling to get the whip hand over the other. First one wins, and then the other; and the two selves keep changing so that I can't recognize them. Often I am unable to tell which self is really thinking and acting, and whether that self has the right to order the other about. At times I avoid the conflict by giving each complete freedom to do as it pleases, without thinking about it. But that doesn't work, for before I know it there is conflict, and one of the two must surrender. The "I" that is speaking feels that God is on his side against all the other "me's." How can I tell which self is the one which God really intends me to have?

Which is really mine? Which belongs to God? In the case of Nero, one self dies and another lives on. In the case of Jonas, the same is true. Silvanus remarked the other evening that repentance means dying to one's own self. But how can one know what true repentance is unless he knows which self must die? Last night one of my selves died and another, entirely new to me, was born. Formerly I would have declared Nero alive and Jonas dead. The new self says that Nero is dead and Jonas alive. But how can the new self be sure that its judgment is God's? Perhaps Nero feels that his too is divine.

Two of Jesus' sayings came into Clement's mind together: "The Son of man must suffer many things, and be rejected, and be killed." "Whosoever would save his life shall lose it, whosoever shall lose his life for my sake shall save it."

Is this the way disciples regard life and death? he thought. *They can bear persecution because the self which the persecutor torments is already dead. They have already said no to that self so that they can also say, "The old self no longer lives, but only the new self which the Messiah gives."*

This awareness so exhilarated Clement that he broke unconsciously into a whistle. He had added nothing to what had happened to him last night, but he had worked his way through difficulties to an understanding of what had happened. God had drawn him into a realm where a new vitality was his, a freedom and a deep thankfulness such as he had never known. God had destroyed the power of false selves to carry on their exhausting battle against the true self.

Suddenly a hearty smile of joy broke over Clement's face as he realized that he had been whistling the chant tune:

> "Neither death, nor life, . . .
> Nor things present, nor things to come . . ."

PART THREE • IN A NEW WORLD

CHAPTER 15

Aftermath

IT REQUIRED days for Clement to become accustomed to the new climate. Each day brought surprises. He hadn't suspected, for example, how important the ordinary acts in the day's routine could become. Facing each choice with a new spirit made him aware of many possibilities. A single angry word or a hasty deed might betray his loyalty to Christ. On the other hand, each simple deed might be motivated by the new loyalty, and thus become a sign that Christ was in control. As long as he submitted each situation to the scrutiny of the new Master nothing could diminish his energy and poise; but a moment of forgetfulness, and he found himself back in the old world of gnawing doubts, short temper, and inner fears. The battle within his own heart between fear and freedom he now realized was a part of the battle which the Messiah was waging in other men's lives as well. Victory in one sector meant victory all along the line.

In another sense, Clement's world had expanded into a marvelously large world. He could no longer think that the whole world turned about himself as its center. Jesus was now the true center, and his world reached as far as God's love. It included all men equally. This world was not organized around self-concern or self-interest. It was organized around a huge program to emancipate all men from their self-imposed narrowness. Clement found himself looking at his companions with different eyes. He was no longer afraid of what they might think of him; rather, he was wondering what Jesus might think of them and do for them. He no longer spent his time sitting in judgment upon their actions and their personalities; rather, he kept trying to understand why they should act that way. Where did their hopes lie, their fears, their loyalties? What were the doors which they were finding closed against them? Were they experiencing the same sense of inadequacy and confusion that he had known, until the Messiah had restored his mind to a single purpose? Yes, each person whom he met became now a part of God's world, where he might see God's mercy trying to break through man's stubborn resistance.

In still another sense, of course, nothing in Clement's world had changed. The work on the Esquiline hill followed its established schedule. Customary habits dictated his daily routine. The circle of friends and work mates remained the same. He himself had witnessed no spectacular vision of angelic visitors, no earthquake of the emotions to jar him loose from the ordinary world. He still lived in a world of work and play, of stones and shops, yes, of emperors and prisons.

Yet it was just the rocklike reality of such things as prisons and crosses which convinced Clement that in his experience of new vitality he was not dreaming. He was actually standing on the threshold of a new world. To be sure, he was still awkward in its presence, quite uncertain about where his next steps would lead. Time would be needed to get his bearings. But the exhilaration that had accompanied his first confession of Christ as his Lord gave him the confidence to meet an unknown future. Full adjustment to the new world would require many weeks. In the meantime, there were immediate tasks to be done.

Most delicate of all was the task of explaining his new situation to those who stood in the world he had left. Clement was too honest to toy with the idea of keeping his decision secret from family and friends. He was too realistic to deceive himself by supposing that they would readily accept his move. What would Sabinus' reaction be—a man so prominent in official circles, so solicitous of the good graces of Nero, so confident of the loyalty of his household? Now to find within his own establishment one of the hated Christians! Would he send Clement back to the country estate or dismiss him entirely? Or would he, as proof of his patriotism, turn him over to Tigellinus? He recalled how Sabinus had warned the Jews of the impending purge, implying his belief in the political innocence of the Christian scapegoats. Yet this was a slender straw on which to rely when winds of hatred and suspicion were so strong.

What would Bar-Joseph say and do? He had known of Clement's interest in Peter. He had even defended the Christians against those Jews who had wanted to turn their names over to the emperor. *I need not fear,* thought Clement, *that Bar-Joseph will turn me over to the police or denounce me publicly. But he will be deeply hurt over my ingratitude and chagrined that I did not follow his ad-*

vice. But I must tell him, and what follows will be up to him.

Most disturbing, however, was the dilemma of how to break the news to his father. How was he to write the reasons for his conversion, how minimize his father's anger and his fear for Clement's safety? His father might even summon him home immediately. Clement had no wish to alienate his family, but the breach was great and might prove irreparable. As a disciple of Jesus, he must be willing to pay the cost, whatever it might be. To give his witness to family and friends seemed at the moment more appalling than the prospect of facing the emperor's police. Perhaps it would be in just such situations, he mused, that he would learn his way around in this new world.

A plan took shape in Clement's mind. He would begin with the more difficult tasks. Tonight he would write the letter to his father; tomorrow evening he would talk with Bar-Joseph. Then, on the third evening, he would go back to the Christian assembly to learn what steps would come next for him as a disciple. Perhaps by then he would know what Sabinus would do. *If God had a hand in my conversion,* he thought, *I can trust him to open other doors when I get to them.*

*   *   *

CLEMENT, TO HIS FATHER MATTATHIAS, GREETING:

I thank God for the report of your good health, and for your continued confidence in me. These recent days have been strenuous, and I have been grateful for the way in which you and my mother have prepared me to meet them.

First of all I must report on the scourge which has overtaken our people in Rome. The public has been demanding that the blame for the fire be fixed and the criminals punished. The emperor's police arrested a large number of Jews and Gentiles for this purpose. The attack was not

directed at the synagogues, as some had feared, but
against the followers of Jesus. Several dozen of these disciples were executed in a public demonstration of horrible
atrocities. So far as I have heard none of your friends
were involved. Since the night of the executions there has
been no more violence. Even the Romans may be sick of
blood.

In my earlier letter I mentioned these followers of Jesus. They believe that the Messiah has come, and that
God is now drawing men into his long-promised Kingdom. You advised me to test their claims by certain questions which you suggested. You will be interested in the
answers which I can now give you. The Christians do not
encourage violent revolt, but apply the rule of love to all
their activities, even to the extent of forgiving their enemies. They do not profit financially from their preaching,
but live simply, supporting themselves. They worship the
God of Israel and seek to obey his commands at any cost.
It is true that they do not require that Gentile converts
obey the Law and the tradition of our elders, but they do
not relax this requirement in order to make life easier for
anyone. Rather, they demand extreme self-denial, as is
proved by their willingness to die for the Messiah.

I do not wish to hide anything from you. Since I received your letter I have been attending their meetings
and have myself become a Christian. It is God's will for
me. Of that I am certain. He has called me to become a
disciple of Jesus—a step which I tried to evade but which
I now have taken. Never have I known such peace and
joy. Never have I been so certain of God's love for his
people and of his faithfulness to his promises to Israel.
What I have done has been done in loyalty to him. I pray
that you may be able to visit Rome soon, for there is much
I should like to discuss with you regarding this whole
matter.

Don't be anxious about my security, for I have no fear
about what lies ahead. I hope that you will rejoice with
me in this new life. Peace be with you and with the other
loved ones at home.

✦　　✦　　✦

The writing of the letter deepened Clement's confidence. He realized a new courage in stating his convictions and in standing by them. *Strange*, he thought, *that tasks which seem difficult at first become easy when I know my own mind. Until now I have always been fighting against myself. Now, although I am fighting against the whole world, I am not afraid. Fears which would have unnerved me a month ago have lost their power. I wonder. Are all fears of external events due really to one's inner uncertainties?*

On the next day Clement's mind was filled with thoughts concerning his coming talk with Bar-Joseph. Although his determination did not waver, the suspense was none the less real. For Bar-Joseph's reaction would indicate the probable response of the entire Jewish community. As trusted elder, his host represented the official world of the synagogue. If he accepted Clement as a Christian, then it might not be impossible to live as a member of both communities. He would not be branded as an enemy of Israel. But if Bar-Joseph ostracized Clement, the ties to the synagogue would be cut, and Clement's fate would foretell the probable fate of the entire Christian Church. Would the synagogue and Church be drawn together by allegiance to a common God and hostility to the world as a common foe; or would synagogue and Church become enemies—with an enmity made the more bitter by the fact that both claimed the same God and the same covenant?

After supper and evening prayers, Clement invited his host to his room, and without delay presented his problem. He recalled Peter's visit to the synagogue, and told of his encounter with the apostle in the Forum. He reminded the elder of their earlier conversation about the apostle's message. He told how he had gone to Jonas' house, how he had himself raised Bar-Joseph's queries and how, one by

one, these objections had been overruled. Then followed
the story of the warnings, the arrests, the executions. Bar-
Joseph listened in silence, sensing the goal to which Clement was leading.

Finally, Clement told him as simply and directly as he
could of his own inner resistance to this strange movement, and of the steps by which this resistance had been
overcome. He ended the narrative abruptly: "So I too am
a disciple of Jesus."

His tone was as cool as if he were describing something
that had happened to someone else. He was not on the
defensive, nor was he defiant. He was not appealing for
the elder's approval, nor was he fearful of his condemnation. Quite apart from his own fears and fancies, Clement
told the story, almost as if he were making the confession
before God rather than before a man.

His host betrayed neither surprise nor anger.

"You know, I suppose, what this decision may mean," he
began. "Are you aware of the danger from the police? This
movement is quite illegal. Do you know too how your
Jewish friends will react? Many of them will hate you
more than they despise pagans."

These questions did not require answers. Nevertheless
Clement replied soberly, "Of course, I know all that."

"Will this faith encourage you to disobey the Law which
God has given Israel?" This did call for an answer, and
Clement was ready. "No," he said firmly. "The Messiah
does not destroy the Law, but fulfills it. God sent his Messiah first to Israel, in fulfillment of his promises to the sons
of Abraham. In my heart I know that it is loyalty to the
prophets which makes me risk rejection by my people,
such rejection as the Messiah himself suffered."

"But doesn't this mean that you will live with the uncircumcised and associate with Gentile sinners?"

"Yes," Clement admitted. "Most Christians are uncir-

cumcised. Most of them—no, all of them—consider themselves sinners. But the question is this: Are they circumcised in heart? Have their sins been forgiven? If God has
forgiven them and drawn them within the bounds of the
covenant, then why should I hesitate to associate with
them? I may be called traitor by those who claim to be
sons of Abraham. But God is Author of the Law, and it is
he who determines who are really the sons of Abraham."

Bar-Joseph was inclined to press this point, to suggest
the danger of relying upon the opinions of the apostles
rather than upon the standards tested by the nation's long
experience. But he realized that it would be useless. He
could tell that any effort to turn Clement aside from his
course would fail. For the time being, at least, the door of
argument was closed. So he turned to more practical
problems.

"I respect your decision, son," he said simply. "May God
help you to choose his path. If you are right, I should be
opposing God to try to change your mind. If you are
wrong, as I think you are, God may have some special
purpose in leading you along this blind path. But where
and how do you plan to live?"

"I have been most grateful to you, sir, for your hospitality. But it would doubtless be embarrassing to you for
me to stay on now as a guest." It was the least Clement
could say, but he hoped in his heart that his gesture would
not be accepted.

"Personally, I should be happy to have you stay here.
You belong to our household, and it would distress me to
have you leave. But I must consider many factors, as you
know. I am regarded in Rome as an elder in the synagogue. I am also responsible for protecting these homeless
people who have found refuge here. In the eyes of the
state, you are now a criminal. What will happen to the

synagogue, to my other guests, if you are found here? As a Christian, you endanger the lives of those with whom you live. Should they be asked to suffer for your sake?"

"I understand," replied Clement. "I shall look for lodgings elsewhere." Though both of them realized the necessity of this decision, neither was pleased with it. It cut across their mutual affection. It made Bar-Joseph appear a discourteous host and made Clement appear an ungrateful guest. It broke bonds which both would gladly have preserved.

"Perhaps," the elder suggested awkwardly, more to cover his embarrassment than to suggest genuine assurance, "perhaps this animosity against Christians will die down. Then you can return without endangering the others. In that case, you will be more than welcome." The conversation ended, and Bar-Joseph left.

The following evening Clement hurried down the now familiar way that led to Jonas' house. What had happened to the disciples since he had last been there? Would he find the house deserted and under guard? Which of his friends would be left? His conscience was uneasy. *Will they think me a traitor? Should I have offered to help in burying the dead?* Yet he was glad that he had stayed away. For one reason, he felt that those who had suffered should be allowed the privacy of sorrow without the intrusion of strangers. For another reason, he had wanted to test himself, to see if he were certain of his discipleship, to see if his courage would stand alone. And he had wanted to bury his own past, to free himself for whatever work might be assigned to him in the coming weeks.

Jonas' widow, Della, welcomed Clement at the door. No words were needed to confirm his fears that Jonas had been killed, nor to show the depth of Della's grief. But, with her husband, she had conquered the fear of death before death came, and she now found the assurance of God's care doubly strong. She spoke quietly of what had happened to the disciples. Forty-two of them had been executed, among whom were eight women and five children. None of the house Churches had been spared; and the membership of some had been so seriously depleted that it was doubtful if they could continue separate meetings. The days had been occupied with emergency duties: gathering the broken bodies, securing graves, burying the remains, notifying friends, taking care of the dependents. All prisoners seemed to have been killed, so there was no longer need to carry food to the jails. But it had taxed their resources to find enough to feed the survivors. Provision must now be made for eighteen widows and twenty-three orphans. No one knew, of course, whether the attacks would continue, or whether the lust for blood had been temporarily satisfied.

As other disciples came in they chatted for a moment with Della and then bowed in prayer. Common sorrows had welded their souls more securely together. The Scriptures, prayers, hymns, and the common meal—all drew a circle enclosing separate sorrows, and at the same time shutting out remorse for the past and anxiety for the future.

After the supper they began to plan for the future. The unity of worship produced a oneness of mind which would have amazed Clement elsewhere, but which seemed entirely natural here. It was the habit of disciples, he learned, to ask for the guidance of Jesus' Spirit before making any decision involving the Church. And it was their custom to refrain from decision if the leading of the Spirit was not clearly manifested to the community as a whole. Each disciple waited in prayer before making any suggestion. Slowly, but with confidence, the decisions were agreed upon.

Della would keep her home as long as the police would permit, and meetings would be held here each evening. Another group of disciples who had been gathering in Aristobulus' home had now to move. Aristobulus had been arrested and the landlord had evicted the family. The widow, Serena, had no means of paying rent elsewhere, and with her two children would share Della's home. Three orphans would also come here to live. In addition, Clement and Silvanus would share a room in this already crowded home, paying enough to enable Della to meet the landlord's fee. The other disciples would help by bringing food for the evening meals. Here also would meet the Christians who had formerly worshiped with Aristobulus.

Since most of those in positions of leadership had been executed, a new assignment of duties became necessary. Here too the worshipers waited for the guidance of God's Spirit before making their choices. Only three of the earlier leaders had been spared. Marcus, on the evening of the arrests, had been absent on an urgent mission to the Churches in Ostia and Pompeii. Though his name was on Tigellinus' list, there had been no effort to track him down. The disciples now decided that he should go immediately to Corinth and Ephesus and other Churches in the east, to tell them about the persecution and to warn them that the disturbance might spread. Rufus was chosen as leader of the evening worship services; Silvanus was asked to supervise the instruction of new converts. This latter group would meet on Sunday mornings. Several men were chosen to serve as deacons, to supervise the common funds, to list the dependents, and to see that no one was missed in the distribution of food. The deacons were busy organizing their work when Clement said good night and left to make his last trip as a guest to Bar-Joseph's home.

CHAPTER 16

A Narrow Road

Hail, sons and daughters! Peace to you in the name of the Lord who loves us."

With this greeting Silvanus addressed the group of students on that first Sunday morning of their "term." "I rejoice that God has called you into the Way of life. Your decision to travel on the Messiah's road and your readiness to risk your lives to his keeping encourage the other pilgrims of our fellowship who have been making this same trek. May your suffering produce steadfastness and your endurance victory. Through Jesus our Lord. Blessed be his name."

Clement looked around at the others and wondered if their inward excitement was as great as his. Even yet, his mind could not catch up with the rapid changes that had taken place in his world. It was less than a week since the night of the martyrdoms, yet here he was—living in a

184

Christian's home, being drawn ever deeper into the mysteries of faith. Now he was beginning systematic training in the disciplines which this strenuous way of life demanded.

I'm glad Silvanus is to be my tutor, he thought. *He will understand my situation, and I can trust his judgment.* Few Christians in Rome, in fact, were better qualified than Silvanus for this post. He had been a companion of Paul in many provinces and had worked closely with Peter in Bithynia and in Rome. He had visited the Church in Jerusalem often, and had become fully acquainted with the preaching and teaching in different cities. His memory was keen, his loyalty unquestioned. Effective in speaking, he could also write whenever the community needed a scribe.

As Clement looked about at the other converts, he realized that the class would tax the teacher's patience. All would have difficult adjustments to make. Sitting near Clement was a somewhat older Jew named Joseph, who had recently moved to Rome from Corinth. Clement recalled that he had seen him in the ranks of the inquirers on several occasions at Jonas' home. He was a wool merchant, having opened a shop in Rome only that spring. Years before, in Corinth, he had first heard of Jesus from Paul, and had even attended a few meetings at the house of Chloe. However, his fear of economic discrimination from fellow Jews had made him cautious. Perhaps the fact that his shop had been destroyed in the July disaster now made him less fearful of poverty.

Gaius was a Gentile from North Africa, a slave in the household of one of the more independent senators, Piso. Well-educated, he had been trusted with the post of librarian and secretary in Piso's staff. Since the fire, he had been in charge of the distribution of food and clothing to people who had lost everything in the fire. It was during this work that Gaius had first met some of the Christian families.

The oldest of the men was Quintus, a professional Roman soldier from a regiment stationed just outside the city gates. He had seen many years of service in Britain and Germany, and was near the age of retiring. Clement could not help wondering how he had been brought to faith in the Messiah. Had his life in the barracks become too empty? Had his spirit been rebelling for years against the futility of violence? Was it the striking contrast of Christian meekness that had left its mark on his mind? Had military life made him so reckless of danger that he was impervious to the cautions of ordinary citizens?

Two women were in the group. Clement had been too reticent to talk much with them. One was a Jewess, still wearing a veil and very shy. She lived across the Tiber, near Bar-Joseph's home, and, like Clement, she had first heard Peter at the Synagogue of the Olive Tree. Her name was Sara. The other girl was a Gentile maid from one of the large estates in Porta Capena. She came in her servant's garb, the cut and fabric of which indicated the high rank of her employer. In fact, she had been given an aristocratic name to indicate the stylishness of the household. She was called Cornelia.

Looking at them, Clement wondered where else in Rome one would come across such a motley group: three Jews and three Gentiles; a mason, a maid, a merchant, a soldier. If they held together, it would be not because of personal congeniality, but because their faith had overcome natural differences of race and class.

Silvanus was beginning his address, and Clement now gave complete attention. "The Church has appointed me to share with you the holy rules by which disciples walk. There is only one Teacher, and all of us are his followers.

He has brought salvation to us. And from day to day, as we need his guidance, he provides light for us to walk in his path. He reminds us of things in the past and points ahead to things in the future so that we may live aright in each present moment. So long as we trust him, he will not lead us astray.

"Let us begin by studying the road itself. Long ago Jeremiah announced:

> " 'Thus saith our God:
>   Behold, I set before you
>   The road of life, the road of death.'

This is the choice to which Jesus has called us. He makes clear the alternatives:

> " 'Wide is the gate; easy to find the road,
>   that leads to destruction,
>   and many are they who take it.
> Narrow is the gate; hard to find the road,
>   that leads to life,
>   and few are they who take it.'

Let us memorize this teaching."

After Silvanus had repeated the lines, the group repeated them with him, several times, until the words were firmly anchored. The rhythm magnetized their tongues, as the meaning crystallized their thoughts. No comment was needed, for vivid in each mind was the narrowness of the gate and the scant few who had found it. They did not need Silvanus' accent to mark the key contrasts: wide—narrow; easy—hard; destruction—life; many—few. Soon, therefore, Silvanus moved on to more detailed instruction.

"You have entered the narrow gate. But do not be deceived by expecting an easy road hereafter. At any moment it is possible to step aside into the road of death. And

always the road to death appears broad and easy. Therefore you must learn how to recognize the entrance to the
narrow road."

"Can you be more specific?" Clement wondered aloud.
"How may we know where to turn from one road to the
other?"

"The first and clearest signpost is the Master's demand
for repentance. The narrow gate always has over it the
words 'Repent, for the kingdom of God is at hand.' At
every step the disciple realizes that he is not worthy of
God's love. That is why he always prays, 'Forgive us our
sins.' But at every step, the disciple discovers that God's
love pursues him with the offer of forgiveness. So all the
pilgrim needs to do is to repent, and he finds himself restored to his place in God's family."

"But what we need to know"—it was Gaius speaking—"is
what does repentance mean?"

"Sometimes it is hard to know what we must do to repent. This is because our sin takes so many different forms.
We may start unconsciously to love ourselves rather than
God. Or we may think too well of ourselves in comparison
with other men. Or we may fear what other men may say
of us and forget God's judgment. We may begin to pity
ourselves because people think ill of us. We may begin
to rely on our own wisdom or power or goodness. Our
attention is turned to trivial things and we forget the major goal. We blame others for our misfortunes and deceive
ourselves about our own importance. We forget that God
loves our enemies as much as he loves us. You see, repentance must be adapted to whatever obstacle has turned
us aside.

"Jesus gave us three proverbs which often help us know
what we must do to repent. If you will fasten these in
your memories, you will find that they fit many situations:

" 'The last shall be first,
And the first shall be last.'

" 'He who exalts himself shall be humbled;
He who humbles himself shall be exalted.'

" 'If anyone wants to be first of all and greatest of all,
Let him become last of all and servant of all.'

Sin makes us want to put ourselves first, repentance makes us willing to put ourselves last. You may remember this most clearly by picturing a little child. Our Lord taught us: 'Whoever will not receive the kingdom of God as a little child will not enter it.' "

Quintus now entered the discussion, slowly selecting words that would express his problem: "Teacher, isn't it absurd to ask an old soldier like me to act like a helpless child? I have been trained in ways of violence. To place myself last and my enemy first would cost me my life, and make me a traitor. How then can I repent except by leaving the army?"

"I am glad that you are taking the teaching seriously," Silvanus commended the soldier. "And Jesus was serious in commanding his disciples, when struck on the one cheek, to turn the other. He demands humility and gentleness of every follower. It is well that you are willing to face frankly how radically Jesus' commands may interfere with your profession."

"Then there is nothing for me to do but resign my post? I'm quite ready to do it for the sake of my new Commander."

"Not too fast," cautioned the teacher. "Wait until your new Commander gives you such an order. I'm not going to answer this question for you, and I want every one of you to understand why I can't."

Turning to the others, he spoke slowly and distinctly:

"Listen carefully, for all of you will face problems exactly similar to this. And all of you will want me to solve those problems for you. Most disciples are keenly disappointed at first, when they discover that there is no clear-cut rule that they can apply to a situation like this. We expect the Messiah to provide us with a complete set of laws, binding on all disciples, so that we could say either that it is right for all Christians to serve in the army or that such service is forbidden to all. But our Leader does not make his road so easy to find as that. And why doesn't he?

"In the first place, he has set each disciple free to make his own decisions, to determine how he shall serve his new Lord. Jesus has a different purpose for each of you in each situation, and your task is to discover that purpose for yourself. There will be many occasions when this responsibility will seem too heavy. You will want someone to lighten your load by laying down specific instructions that will solve your problem for you. And you will meet other Christians who will infringe upon your freedom by telling you just what you must do. Beware of those Christians. Only one person has a right to do that—our Lord.

"In the second place, however, I must make it clear that Jesus has given us this freedom for a definite purpose. He wants us to use it in serving others and not ourselves. Every occasion is an opportunity to serve our Master by serving our brothers in love. We belong to him—our bodies, our motives, our acts. And he wants to use us in carrying on his work among men."

"There's the nub of my problem," agreed the soldier. "I now know that I am free either to stay in the army or to leave it. But I don't yet know which is God's will for me."

"And it is at this point that repentance provides you with the key to the gate that opens into the narrow road. If you are humble, you will not choose the line of least resistance. You will not ignore the obligation to love even your enemies. You will not become arrogant over your power. You will constantly ask the right questions: What is my attitude now toward the Messiah? toward myself? toward other men? And if you raise those questions, you will constantly be listening for the Messiah to answer them. Then he *will* answer them.

"It is possible, Quintus, that he will want you to resign your post. If so, it would be proof of your pride and cowardice if you refused. But he may want you to stay in the army. If so, that does not mean an easier road, for you would still be tempted to place yourself first and to hate your enemies. Your Master knows how difficult it is for a soldier to follow him."

"My life as a Christian would be simpler outside of the army," replied Quintus. "The rest of you don't have to put up with the brutality and arrogance of a military life."

"I'm not so sure," objected Joseph. And Gaius nodded quick agreement.

"Neither am I so sure," was Silvanus' answer. "The army is not the only place where brutality and arrogance are the rule. If we tried to find an occupation free from selfish pride, we should have to leave the world entirely. Every institution is permeated by sin. But the disciple's job is not to search for a place where there is no evil. Had Jesus done that, he would not have come to deliver us. If we copy him, we shall not shun the burden of the world's evil, but accept it. We are following One who remained humble in the midst of evil, and who thus transformed it. Remember this: It is not possible for us to escape the world's corruption, but it is always possible to repent."

"It seems to me"—and this was Joseph speaking—"that my situation is more baffling than Quintus'. How can I think always of the other fellow in buying and selling

wool? To make a profit, I must buy cheap and sell dear.
And to sell my stuff, I must make the claim that my workmanship is superior to my competitors'. And sometimes I
know that that is not true. It was difficult enough to stay
in business as a loyal Jew. Now, as a Christian, it seems
completely impossible." There was a note of real anxiety
in his voice; it was easy to see that he feared bankruptcy
in his new calling.

"There's no good to be gained in mincing words or in
deceiving ourselves," was the sharp rejoinder. "The Christian way is not always what you or I should like to make
it, Joseph. It is not we who lay down the terms, but the
Messiah. And you are not the first to be baffled by the conditions he laid down.

"Once a rich man came to Jesus, asking what he must
do to gain a place in the Kingdom of God. Jesus said: 'You
know what the commandments are.' 'Yes, Teacher,' was
the reply. 'Ever since I was a boy I have followed them.'
Then Jesus, in his love for the man, said: 'You must do one
more thing. Go, sell your holdings, and give the money to
the poor. Then come and follow me. You will thus receive
riches which you can never lose.' But the man was unwilling to do this, and sadly departed. Do you know what Jesus
said to his disciples? 'You see how hard it is for men with
money to enter the Kingdom! It is easier for a camel to go
through a needle's eye than for a rich man to enter the
kingdom of God.' "

"Then how can anyone who is not penniless be a disciple?"

"That's just what the first disciples asked Jesus. And
what did he answer? He did not say that no rich man could
be his disciple. Rather, he said that 'all things are possible
with God.' But let us understand first of all why Jesus
found it so difficult to enlist rich men in his company. How

easy it is for a rich man to become the unconscious slave of his possessions! He is tempted to fear poverty more than he fears God; he actually is betrayed into thinking that his life depends upon his income. No matter how fully he believes he has been obeying the Commandments, his allegiance to Mammon displaces his allegiance to God. If he is not willing to sacrifice everything that he possesses for the sake of the Kingdom, that is proof that he does not actually love God with his whole heart. And when this is a man's condition, it takes a miracle for God to change his heart so that he prefers the Kingdom to all else.

"And this miracle is worked in the act of repentance. The Messiah does not arbitrarily 'command' every disciple to leave his business, any more than he commands every soldier to leave the army. But he does demand—yes, and arbitrarily too—that every disciple at every moment, if he wishes to walk the narrow way, must enter by the gate of repentance. Should he want you, Joseph, to continue your woolen shop, this repentance will utterly change your attitude toward your work. And it will protect you from being corrupted by the pride and glory of wealth. It will enable you to use all your resources to the glory of God."

Turning to the others, Silvanus commented: "Joseph's problem is a real one, but it is actually no greater than the problem every one of us faces. What Jesus said of wealth applies to every form of self-importance. It is equally true that it is easier for a camel to go through a needle's eye than for a *proud* man to enter the Kingdom of God. Desire for our own financial advantage is only one of the more obvious lures that tempt us to glorify ourselves rather than God."

Cornelia spoke: "How my owner would scoff at the folly of this teaching on humility! He doesn't care much about gaining or saving money, but he loves to spend it. His

chief ambition is to be known as the most lavish host in
Rome. He wants to entertain his aristocratic guests as if
each one were the emperor. He worships the rules of eti-
quette. Yesterday he ordered twenty lashes for one of us
who offended a guest by seating him in the wrong place,
and ten lashes for another who spilled a bowl of soup."

Silvanus interrupted her. "You see, it is always easier to
see how someone else needs repentance than how we ourselves do. It is true enough that Cornelia's master would
find the Kingdom's gate very narrow. I recall this parable
of Jesus on hospitality:

> "'When you make a feast and invite guests, don't invite
> members of your family, friends, or rich neighbors. They
> will repay you by returning the invitation. Invite rather
> the poor, the lame, the crippled, the blind, who are not
> able to return your invitation. And you will be repaid in
> the day of resurrection, and you will be blessed.'

"But Cornelia's master is not a disciple, and Cornelia is.
It will be Cornelia's tendency to express her selfishness in
other ways, and it is her responsibility as a disciple to think
first of her own need for repentance. For example, she may
show partiality in her own treatment of friends. She may
resent the fact that she is given so low a ranking in the
social scale. She may think of herself as superior to other
slaves. As slaves, you will find it difficult to treat everyone
as an equal within our fellowship. The habits of a lifetime
are not easily broken. Most people say, 'To be impartial
won't get you anywhere!' Our Messiah says, 'It is a sin
to be partial.'

" 'If a man attends our assembly wearing expensive jew-
els and clothing, and another comes in a ragged and
patched garment, and you pay special attention to the
first, saying, "Here is a good seat," you make false distinc-

tions, and become judges according to the world's standards. If you say to the poor man, "Stand there," or, "Sit at my feet," you blaspheme the name of our Messiah. You disobey his command to love your neighbor as yourself.'

"If the disciple is to understand his neighbor's need he must get his mind off himself. Only by forgetting ourselves can we remember our neighbor and our God. Otherwise the gnat of self-interest gets into our eyes and blinds us to God's love. Only the humble man can keep the line of vision open between himself and God."

It was Sara who spoke now. "I can see how this teaching revolutionizes pagan practice. But how does it differ from the teaching of our rabbis? They too urge us to confess our sins. And in our daily prayers we ask God's forgiveness. In fact, what Jesus said about the needle's eye reminds me of one of our sayings:

"'Open for me a gate of repentance as large as a needle's eye,
And I will make it wide enough for chariots and horses.'"

Clement was grateful for Sara's question, and he listened closely, thinking of the sincere humility of Bar-Joseph and his father.

"Yes, the rabbis teach the Law and the Prophets, and they find there God's command. And our pride would trap us if it prompted us to assert our superiority over the rabbis in this matter. Notice how repentance is destroyed the moment we say to ourselves. 'I am more penitent than my neighbor.'

"But isn't this just the trap into which so many of our brothers have fallen? Is it not pride that makes some men think that Israel is more righteous than the Gentiles? Does not a rabbi become guilty of partiality if he claims superi-

ority over publicans and sinners? Does not blindness result
from his assurance that God will save the law-abiding but
punish the lawbreakers? True repentance is impossible
when we think we have earned God's approval by obeying
the Law. Yes, we may do more than the Law demands and
confess our sins every day, yet still fall short of true repentance. We may still select chief seats, still demand
places of prestige, still hide from ourselves our major sin
by correcting our minor sins, still be engaged in exalting
ourselves over other men, still be thinking only of a few
past misdeeds rather than of our present unworthiness to
enter God's Kingdom. The test is this: Do we use our
prayers to puff ourselves up, or do we express in them
the fact that our self-importance has been done away
with?

"Like the rabbis, it is easy for us to use our good deeds
to reinforce our good opinion of ourselves. But our Master
does not tolerate this use of faith. He levels the fences by
which we attempt to preserve our pride. The place where
we build these fences is our heart. Our inner self asserts its
superiority. But Jesus penetrates this inner circle and
makes us realize that even here we are unworthy of God's
love. The self in which we boast is seen to be sinful. And
it was to save that self from pride that Jesus died.

"When a man repents, he surrenders this citadel and the
fences by which he has tried to protect it. He admits that
at his best he is unworthy of God's love. As a sinner he
opens the doors to God, begs forgiveness, and is at last
ready to receive God's help.

"When he does this, of course, he becomes a threat to the
inner conscience of other men. For they are not ready to
let down the bars. Their pride prevents a surrender. They
want to believe that God will give them first place. When
God chooses a sinner instead, they resent such unjust treat-

ment. And they give vent to their resentment by hating the man who has thus received forgiveness.

"Jesus cast this inner drama into a story of a father who had two sons:

" 'The younger said, "Father, give me my share of the inheritance." And the father divided his estate. Soon the son left home for a distant country, and there wasted his inheritance in reckless living. When he had spent it all, a famine struck that country and he began to be hungry. He got a job with one of the citizens and was sent to the farm to feed hogs. He became so hungry that he would have been glad to eat the hog food. And no one would help him. Then he confronted himself: "My father's servants have plenty to eat, but I starve. I will go back home and tell my father, 'I have sinned against God and against you. I am not worthy to be your son, but take me back as a servant.' " And he returned home. While he was still a long way off, his father saw him coming. He ran out to meet him and gave him a hearty welcome. The son said to him: "Father, I have sinned against God and against you. I am not worthy to be your son." But his father called his servants and instructed them: "Give him the finest clothes and shoes. Prepare our fattest calf for a great celebration. My dead son has come back to life. My lost son has been found." And they began to celebrate his return. " 'But the older son, who had been working in the fields, came back to the house. When he heard the merriment, he asked one of the servants the cause of it. "Your brother is back," the servant replied, "and your father is celebrating his return." The older brother was peeved, and would not go in. So his father came after him. He complained to his father: "I have been serving you for years, obeying your every wish. And not yet have you honored me with a banquet for my friends. But now that your other son has come back, after wasting your money on harlots, you have given to him the best of everything." To this his father replied, "Son, all that I have is yours. But it is only right to celebrate. Your dead brother has come back to life. Your lost brother has been found." ' "

"This story," continued Silvanus, "gives us one picture of repentance as the way by which we make ourselves small enough to enter the needle's eye. But the truest picture, one from which we cannot escape, is the picture of our Lord. In him repentance was perfect. Though he was Lord of all, he became Servant of all. He was first of all, yet he became last of all. He humbled himself so far as to die, a slave on the cross. You see, brothers, what an example God has given us. Since our Lord is so humble, what ought we to be who have come under his yoke?

"This must be our prayer at every instant: 'Forgive us our sins; thy kingdom come.' The first reminds us to forget everything in the past—yes, to forget ourselves, knowing that we possess nothing of our own. The second reminds us that there is only one direction, one leader, one prize— life in God's Kingdom.

"Noah preached repentance; those who obeyed were saved. Jonah foretold destruction to Nineveh; the penitent were reconciled and received salvation. Jesus came to seek sinners, and poured out his blood for our salvation. He gives to us the grace of repentance.

> "'Wide is the gate; easy to find the road,
>   that leads to destruction,
>   and many are they who take it.
> Narrow is the gate; hard to find the road,
>   that leads to life,
>   and few are they who take it.'"

CHAPTER 17

Another Narrow Road

As CLEMENT left the house of Jonas, hurrying to work, the teachings he had been hearing continued to occupy his mind. *One thing is clear,* he thought. *My chief battle will be with myself, not with others. Tilts with Nero do not come every day, but tilts with one's own weaknesses do. It really doesn't matter what Sabinus will say; what really does matter is how I will respond to his decision. Will I accept his opposition as an opportunity or will I resent it? Julian's Stoic teachers are surely right in this, that a man first of all must become master of his own passions.*

Even this thought, however, did not make him less eager to learn Sabinus' decision. Yesterday he had asked his employer if he could begin work two hours later on Sunday mornings, provided he worked overtime two other days. In making the request he had explained without hesitation his reason.

"You see, sir, I have become a disciple of the Christians, and that is the time each week for instruction in the faith."

"A Christian!" Sabinus had been unable to believe his ears. Then he had given way to a fit of laughing. "That's a good one. I've heard a good many excuses for coming late to work, but this is the best yet."

Then when he had looked at Clement's serious face, he had caught himself sharply: "You can't really mean that you *are* a Christian. Have you forgotten so soon what the emperor did to them?"

Clement had been prepared for anything but ribald derision. His cheeks had burned with instinctive irritation. Ridicule was harder to bear than physical violence. Only with great difficulty had he been able to control his temper.

"Am I serious? Never more so in my life. On the evening Nero killed his helpless victims, I became a Christian."

Sabinus had found even this straight-faced declaration hard to accept. "You of all people," he deplored. "I have always counted on you as one of the most dependable workers. Now to have you infected with this fantastic superstition!"

"I don't think you'll find me any less dependable. And how do you know that this is a fantastic superstition? After all, I know something about these Christians—perhaps more than you do. Would I stake my life on a whim or a crazy fad? However, I didn't intend to get tangled up in an argument about my faith. I simply wanted to ask you for one favor. If you want me to stay on this job, I should like the privilege of coming late on Sunday mornings. I assure you that I will not abuse the privilege."

Sabinus had stalled for time in which to decide. "Do the other workers know?"

"Only Julian, I think."

"Does your father know?"

"I have written him."

"What am I to do? It's more than a matter of letting you change your hours on Sunday. Can you see how vulnerable my position is? Just imagine. Less than a week ago the Christian leaders were killed as enemies of the state. Now I, a city commissioner, permit the sedition to get rooted within my own staff. Any night a detective may observe you at a secret meeting of these criminals, and may follow you here to my estate on the Esquiline, within a stone's throw of the emperor's palace. Nothing could be more foolhardy than for me to keep you on. Yet you have always been trustworthy. No, I won't decide today. Come late tomorrow if you wish, and then I shall let you know. But, in the name of Jupiter, keep your mouth shut. When Nero gets a whiff of rumor, he snuffs out a man's life as easily as he blows out a candle."

There they had left the matter. Now today they would have to settle it. What would today's interview bring? *At least,* thought Clement, as he waited for his employer, *I won't have to endure that raucous laughing. And Silvanus has prepared me for remaining humble, whatever Sabinus may have decided.*

When he reported at his employer's headquarters, he found that Sabinus' emotions were under better control. He had evidently determined to confine discussion to matters of business. He could not afford to be drawn into a debate on the merits of this new cult. The law was the law, and he must be prudent if he flouted it. In the interim, however, Sabinus had made discreet inquiries. He had found that the police were desisting for the present from further prosecutions. He had also satisfied himself that Clement had thus far created no disturbance among the other workers. Secretly, he was a bit amused over his own predicament. He was not averse to a bit of excitement. Nor was he too fearful of snubbing the police, if he could do it with relative safety. After all, Nero was as fickle in his hatreds as in his loves. The extremity of police brutalities had encouraged in Sabinus, as in other citizens, a reaction toward tolerance.

Clement is not a cur, he assured himself. *And there is no reason to treat all dogs as if they are curs.*

The interview, accordingly, passed very quickly. "What would you say to this bargain?" Sabinus asked Clement. "Let's continue the present arrangement for perhaps two weeks. Of course, I may have to discharge you at any moment. And if you are arrested, I shall disclaim any knowledge of your illegal activities. On your part, I want you to promise that you will not try to spread this faith among my staff."

"Does that mean that I cannot talk with Julian about it?"

"No, that won't matter. But there must be no agitation, no disturbance. Then too I want you to promise not to tell anyone, not even Julian, that I know anything about your membership in this cult."

"My covenant forbids me to lie," replied Clement. "However, we are taught not to endanger the lives of others by giving evidence to the police, even under torture. And we are taught to take full responsibility for our faith. You can count on me to do that."

Both being satisfied with this arrangement, they parted, not, however, without a word of gratitude from Clement for his employer's courtesy.

If I were in his shoes, he wondered later, *would I have taken this risk? He has nothing to gain, and everything to lose. I hope he will not be sorry.*

When he joined Julian, who had been working on the

house alone for two hours, Julian asked at once why Clement was late.

"You gave me a real fright this morning," he began. "When you didn't come to work, I was afraid you had been arrested."

"Nothing so exciting as that," Clement replied. "Each Sunday morning I plan to study under my new tutor. Today was the first lesson."

Because they were behind with the work the two men concentrated on the job of catching up with the schedule. But at lunch time Julian returned to the earlier subject by asking, "What was the topic of your lesson this morning?"

"The humility of a Christian. What repentance means in our attitude toward others and toward ourselves. You know, I found myself wondering how the Christian teaching compares with the Stoic teachers about whom you talk. You are always quoting Seneca. Does he say anything about penitence?"

Clement hoped to shift the lead in the conversation to his friend and thus by-pass the areas forbidden by Sabinus and at the same time enable him to think further on the topic of the morning's study.

"I've just been rereading Seneca's letters," Julian answered, indicating by his voice that he would welcome a discussion on this subject. "They are packed with advice on what our attitude should be toward others. Seneca says, for example, a good deal about which men are superior and which are inferior. The one who fears death is inferior; the one who scorns it is superior. We are conquered by what we fear; we conquer what we do not fear."

"Then you would agree that Peter was superior to Nero? Nero fears any opposition; Peter feared only that he might betray the Messiah."

"Yes, perhaps Seneca would agree to that in principle,

though I doubt if he would approve Peter's motives. He believes that men should not even fear God. As a philosopher, he sees that all men are equal, because every day death is equally close to all. Any day the richest man may be killed by his slave. Or, as he puts it in one place, the ship which wins the race today may founder tomorrow. Only the man who masters the fear of death is superior."

"Peter had a very different reason for accepting death," Clement replied, finding it difficult to choose the right words. "He didn't want to prove himself superior to Nero. And he didn't look upon death with cool indifference. He really did not want to die any more than I do. I think he was enabled to face death unafraid because his Master had been crucified for him. Jesus' Spirit exerted over him a power greater than the power of Nero. Seneca may be too proud to be disturbed by death. Christians are too humble to be surprised or alarmed by it."

"No, pride is one thing that Seneca does not tolerate," Julian replied quickly. "No proud man can be content with what he has. The rich man desires to be known everywhere as the richest man; hence he is always seeking more wealth. But this craving makes him inferior to his slave, if his slave is content with what he has. According to Seneca, you as a freedman can become the only true aristocrat in an assembly of senators. A slave can free himself from cares and worries, while his master enslaves himself in passions and fears—and these fetters get all the tighter as he hurries through life. In fact, Seneca tells Lucilius that he could name a consul who is slave to an old hag, a wealthy man who is slave to a servingmaid, and a powerful ruler who is in serfdom to pantomime players. He doesn't give names, but almost anyone would know that this last slave is the emperor himself."

"That sounds to me like a subtle form of pride," replied

Clement. "Seneca seems to feel that a man should consider himself more important than the whole world. By feeding his own independence and wisdom, the wise man arrives at a point where he can gloat over the folly of everyone else. Silvanus told us that the Christian must reduce his self-importance to zero."

"Aren't you confusing pride and dignity?" Julian questioned. "Naturally Seneca insists on man's innate dignity. In his description of the wise king, Seneca says every man can trace his ancestry back to the gods. He agrees with Plato that every king comes from a race of slaves, and every slave has a king among his ancestors. Each of us may become a king by acting in a manner worthy of a king. We must be loyal to that which is royal in ourselves. We must exalt our royal ancestry. But that is our dignity, not our pride."

Clement pondered Julian's defense of the nobility of every man. He was forced to admire his independent tone, but he found himself trying to capture the elusive difference between it and the teaching of Silvanus. His attention fixed itself on the word "exalt." Perhaps this word held the answer.

"What you say about each man being a king reminds me of a saying of Jesus which I learned this morning:

" 'He who exalts himself shall be humbled;
He who humbles himself shall be exalted.'

Seneca says that to be happy a man must feel satisfied with his own achievement of superior virtue. The happy man will be proud, not of his status in society, but of his own inner goodness. Silvanus says almost the opposite—that the worst form of pride is our own self-love, our own attempt to convince ourselves that we are better than we are. As Christians, we realize that at our best we are unworthy sinners, not worthy wise men. What does Seneca say on this point?"

"Of course, he insists that every man must confess his faults. If you do not recognize mistakes, you are still in their clutches, like a dreamer who does not know that he is asleep. And vices love to parade themselves as virtues, just as dreams are most deceptive when they seem most real. But it is only by loyalty to our virtues that we can root out the vices. We should never repent of our virtues. To be happy we must deserve happiness by forsaking all other desires. When we are true to our best self, then we are happy."

"But how does an evil man know which is his best self? And how do I know that this best self is good enough to stand in the presence of God?"

"Oh, Seneca insists that every man is created by God! God has implanted in each of us a spark of divine reason, a fragment of divine goodness. This is what makes us all equal. This spark of divine reason is the soul. To each of us God entrusts this soul as an orphan for us to take care of. We must train it as we would train a most beloved son. To consider this orphan unworthy would be treason to God."

"How do we train this orphan?"

"By training ourselves in the life of virtue. Just as the sick man forgets his business duties and stops fretting about minor matters, trying only to get well, so the sick mind should say farewell to all other interests in its desire to become healthy. Philosophy is the only doctor with medicine for the soul. The doctor must be given power to arrange our daily schedules and to determine our diet and exercise. Philosophy, as the physician of the soul, is the only master whose commands we should follow."

"Then we should be good philosophers," laughed Clement, "for we have certainly been neglecting business for this conversation. But I think Sabinus would prefer working men to wise men. We'd better get back to work."

"Yes, but maybe we are meant to be philosophers," replied Julian, reluctant to leave the conversation. "As Seneca puts it: 'Philosophy keeps saying to all other occupations: I do not intend to take the time which you leave idle. I shall allow you to keep only the time which I shall leave.'" But with this parting shot, Julian took up his tools.

Clement, too, bent to his task with vim. But his mind continued to toss these competing thoughts about. He could see the greatness of Seneca's teaching. Like the Christians, Seneca advocated a narrow road. Like Jesus, he called his disciples to strenuous sacrifices. But the more he talked with Julian the more certain he became that the two roads had different starting points and different destinations. Does philosophy, for all its greatness, lead one to be proud of his wisdom and virtue? And does this pride exclude a man from God's Kingdom? Does Seneca's road lead to dignity or vanity? Does repentance destroy man's dignity or actually open the way to the true dignity? How does the disciple who humbles himself become exalted?

If every day goes like this, he reflected, *I shall have enough questions stored up by Sunday to keep Silvanus busy.*

Not only that day, but each day of the week, sped by like lightning. Each moment was so full of interest to Clement that he did not notice time's flight. Before he knew it, the time for the second session with his tutor had come.

CHAPTER 18

Giving and Forgiving

Peace to you all in Christ!

"Why do I say 'in Christ'? I look around and greet you—Quintus, Gaius, Joseph, Clement, Cornelia, Sara. Yet when I greet you *in Christ,* I am saying that each of you is a different person in Christ's eyes than in the world's eyes. In Christ each of you has a new name. Each of you has been born again; in each a new self is emerging. When you were baptized into Christ, you bade farewell to the old self. When he entered your life by dying for you, he created in your heart a new desire, a new hope, a new set of duties, a new kinship with his disciples. He made you a member of his body, because from him you have received power to live as his instrument. Thanks be to God for sharing with us the life of his Son."

After this introduction Silvanus asked the students at what points during the preceding week they had found it

most difficult to hold to the new course. Clement's thoughts
flew back to what Julian had said about the royal orphan
which, according to Seneca, had been given to each man
to nurture. Not that this had tempted him. Rather, it had
interested him and made him eager to discover differences
between Silvanus' teaching and Seneca's.

Already he knew part of the answer. For to Silvanus the
true self of the Christian is not the noble germ of reason
which every man receives at birth. No, this true self is the
new life that begins in conversion, born according to the
pattern of the Messiah's love. This self depends upon Jesus'
death and Resurrection; it is nurtured by sharing the cross
in repentance and forgiveness. What takes place in conversion is not finding a philosopher to train man's innate reason, but response to a Saviour who forgives sin. The new
self is not something inherited by nature, but a new gift
from the Messiah.

While these connections were being forged in Clement's mind, the other initiates were engaged in more direct
confessions. The freedom with which they answered the
teacher's query showed how completely he had won their
confidence. Quintus told how he had been aroused by the
cynical byplay of the other soldiers, who continued to
make filthy jests about the Christians whom they had killed
in the arena. They had discussed the lurid details with
lewd enjoyment. The more horrible the penalty, the more
sport it provided for their mockery.

"I began to feel," Quintus confessed, "that I was vastly
better than these brutes. I began to hate them for their
gloating. Such beasts are surely outside the range of God's
mercy. How can we forgive such animals? And must we
not use violence to defend ourselves against them?"

"Unless we forgive them, we have no right to expect
God to forgive us. Unless we forgive them, we are not

wholly repentant concerning our own shortcomings before God."

So Silvanus answered, aware that it was too vague and too glib an answer. But he asked Quintus to wait for a fuller discussion.

When Gaius had a chance, he described the tensions he had experienced in his work in the poorer sections of the city. "How easy to repent in our worship services," he observed, "but how difficult to do so when I am at work! Here hungry men yap over the bones like so many hounds, willing, it seems, to use their teeth to rip open the throat of a hungrier neighbor. I realize that Jesus loved the unlovely, but it seems impossible for me to love these human derelicts."

Gaius went on to say how he also detested the opposite group, for whom he worked—the rich who gorged themselves at lavish banquets and then threw the crumbs to the starving in order to keep them contented. What hope could there be for these two groups, the richest and the poorest? "I caught myself thinking how superior I am to both groups."

"What made you catch yourself?" asked the teacher.

"Jesus' picture of the Pharisee and the tax collector."

Cornelia had waited to speak until the men had finished. "I found a different sort of obstacle," she said now. "I had supposed that it would be quite easy for me to act as one of the humblest, for, after all, I am only a slave. I was so busy doing various tasks for my owner, Lateranus, that there was little time to think of myself as a follower of Jesus.

"And so I began to chafe under the conditions of my work. I began to resent having to run useless errands for everybody, always fawning before guests and doing their menial tasks. Like Gaius, I felt superior to them, and especially now that I have something more important to do with my time. Why should a disciple of Christ be forced to use all her energy and time on meaningless and trivial errands?"

Silvanus now took over the discussion. "You see how right I was in predicting last week that you would find many obstacles in the way of repentance. Christ always confronts us when we have followed our own wills, when we have failed to follow him. And he calls us to return and ask for his forgiveness. When you feel superior to the people for whom you work, Gaius and Cornelia, you indicate your refusal to forgive them. Yet each temptation to hate others, each mood of self-pity or pride, is an opportunity to hear God's call anew and to open the door again to his power. Only he can cause us to repent our own unworthiness. And only then do we find that we can forgive others.

"This is the rule of our fellowship which we must explore today: 'Even as the Lord forgave you, do you also forgive.' Note that there are three links in the chain of forgiveness. It begins with the Lord, who treated enemies as friends and died for them. Then it comes from the Lord to us. When the Messiah forgives us, we receive a new self. Like the Apostle Paul, we can say, 'I no longer live, but Christ lives in me.'

"Then comes the third link: Christ in us forgives our enemies. Otherwise he does not yet live in us. There are always three persons involved: the Lord, yourself, and your worst enemy. Eliminate any one of the three and true forgiveness becomes impossible.

"Quintus, what you need to remember when the soldiers mock at their victims is this: How did Jesus treat his enemies as they were killing him? And how does he treat you? As the prophet foretold of him:

" 'When he was reviled, he did not revile in return;
　　When he suffered, he did not threaten.
　　　He carried our sins in his sufferings on the tree,
　　　That we might die to sin and live to righteousness.'

"This, then, is the general principle by which we must
react to all enemies. Repeat it after me:

" 'You have put off the old self with his doings.
　　Put to death therefore earthly things
　　　Wherein you used to walk:
　　Anger, wrath, malice, slander, foul talk, lying.

" 'You have put on the new self in the creator's image.
　　Put on, therefore, heavenly things,
　　　Where Christ lives:
　　Compassion, kindness, meekness, patience, forbearance,
　　　forgiveness.
　　Above all things, put on love, for love binds all these
　　　duties together in perfect harmony.'

"If you will recall the situations that Quintus and Gaius
and Cornelia described, you will notice that we take the
first misstep when we start to compare ourselves with
others. That is the mark of self-love and pride, even
though we recognize that these others may be more worthy
than we. And you will notice that this tendency loses its
grip when we contrast our old self and the new self which
is given by Christ. That is the mark of repentance, to see
oneself before God, the old self trying to hold on to the
past, the new self trying to act according to the mind of
Christ. When we become absorbed in this warfare on the
inside, we worry less about our enemies on the outside.

"The more we love, the more the world will hate us,
　　As it hated our Master.
　The more it hates us, the more will we be tempted to
　　hate it,
　　As our Master was tempted;

The more we resist this temptation, the more is God's
love exhibited in us,
As the Master exhibited it on the cross.
The more difficult it becomes, the more necessary
If Christ is to rule our actions.

"Hear the command of our Lord:

" 'Love your enemies,
Do good to them who hate you,
Give to him who asks you.

" 'For if you love men who love you,
what thanks have you?
Even sinners do that much.
If you do good to men who do good to you,
what thanks have you?
Even sinners do that much.
If you lend to men of whom you hope to receive,
what thanks have you?
Even sinners do that much.
Be merciful, even as your Father is merciful.'

"To this rule, Jesus made no exception. Once an exception is allowed, the whole rule becomes worthless. Among
friends we don't need the rule. We need it only among enemies. But the more we need it the more difficult it is to
follow. Gaius is inclined to exclude the swine and dogs;
Quintus wants to make an exception for brutal and foul-
mouthed soldiers; Cornelia would like to exclude the
finicky people whom she serves. But if you exclude anyone,
at that instant you have put on the old self and have put
off the new life in Christ."

Joseph, who had kept silent until now, spoke: "That is
a hard saying, teacher. But I find that the hardest command is one which so far you have not made clear: 'Give
to him who asks you.' Surely there are exceptions to that
rule. Must we give money to every beggar, and lend our

money without expecting any return from the borrower?
How can that be?"

"I suppose this saying, Joseph, is one of the most difficult of all Jesus' demands. Certainly it is one that causes
trouble for every disciple. Many times it will seem to you
that faith creates more problems than it solves. But you
must remember that Christ did not die to solve all the
problems of living in this age, so that his disciples could be
safe from difficulties of the sort you mention.

"Faith, then, does not furnish a ready-made solution to
your problem, Joseph. Some disciples have been called
of God to sell all their possessions. Some have been called
to continue their occupations. There is no fixed rule except
this—that each disciple must seek for himself the mind of
Christ. Christ has set us free, but he has made it clear
that his disciples cannot serve both God and Mammon.
Not every disciple is penniless, but any man who *fears*
poverty more than he fears displeasing the Messiah is unfit
for the Messiah's Kingdom. Woe to the disciple who prefers the saving of money to the serving of Christ. Where
his treasure is, there his heart is also.

"In any case, one disciple must not judge another in this
matter. It is Christ alone who is our Judge. It is Joseph's
task as a disciple to seek Christ's verdict, and to decide
what he must do in order to obey his Lord.

"The Lord saves us by making clear the conflict between
the love of the world's way and the love of God's way.
Each of us stands at the point where God's Kingdom in-
vades the world. To lend only if the borrower will return—
that is the way the world safeguards its future. To lend
without assurance of return—that is the way the Kingdom
faces its future. So, when a man asks us for help, we
may ask ourselves: Is not this actually what God has done
for us, given us everything in exchange for nothing? Is not

this actually what Jesus does for us, every time we pray in his name, 'Forgive us our debts, as we forgive our debtors'?

"Now notice what happens to the rule if you exclude money from the command to forgive. It is right, you say, for Cornelia to forgive personal slights and for Gaius to overlook the depravity of the people who come to him for help. But it is wrong for me to cancel financial obligations. What now? Doesn't that mean that you give to money a higher value than to personal injuries and moral character? You are willing to love men, so long as they pay their debts to you. If God did that, wouldn't he limit his mercy to men who are solvent? Are we to forgive only as long as it costs us nothing in material terms?

"Whatever our answers may be, there is no doubt about what Jesus taught.

" 'If a man takes away your overcoat, give him your coat
        as well.
    If a man compels you to go with him a mile, go two.
    When you give, don't let one hand know what the other
        is doing.'

"If there is no exception, are there limits to this giving?" Joseph was still in doubt. "I can see how a man should give away all he can spare. None of us really *needs* any great amount of money. But if we apply this rule without limit, shysters will take advantage of us until we are penniless. Then we could neither help the needy nor support ourselves."

"As long as we live in the old world, we must consider those possibilities. But Jesus wasn't concerned with maintaining a safe balance, but with confronting us with God's commands. One day Peter (who was as cautious as you, Joseph) was trying to get Jesus to state the limit. He asked: 'How many times shall I forgive a man? Is seven times enough?' 'No,' answered Jesus, 'seventy times seven.' Jesus scorned a calculating spirit of that kind. We should forgive more times than we can count, without caring to count.

"What happens when you begin to count? Is it forgiveness to say to a man, 'I forgive you,' and to say secretly to yourself: 'I will forgive him seven times, but no more. Then let him look out, for I will get even'? Is that the way in which God counts our sins? Or shall I figure this way: 'I have ten thousand dollars. I don't need all that to live on; two thousand dollars will support me. I will, therefore, give away eight thousand dollars, carefully, wisely, slowly. But after that, no one need expect anything from me'? Does such an attitude really represent forgiveness of debts in gratitude for God's forgiveness of our debt? In such calculations, am I thinking as a man of the world, or as one who has been born again into God's Kingdom? Is this cautious self-concern, this unwillingness to risk too much— is it a mark of the new life, in the image of the Messiah?

"No, when I take that attitude and come to worship the Lord, he sits as a judge and points his finger directly at that one reservation. He says to me, 'How much do you love me?' And I become aware that I actually love him only so far but no farther. Then I realize that I cannot expect him to forgive me unless I forgive. I cannot receive his supreme gift so long as I limit the amount of my giving. He doesn't say to me: 'Show me that you love me by giving a few gifts and forgiving a few people; then, after a while you can forget about that requirement. I am willing to overlook it, once you have provided a decent token of your affection.' No. What he says is this:

"'If you are offering a gift at the altar, and recall that your brother has anything against you, leave your gift there. Go, be reconciled first to your brother. Then come and offer your gift.'

"This is just the way the Kingdom disturbs our cautious arrangements. Just when we have satisfied ourselves that we have sacrificed enough, then God comes with his supreme gift and discloses that those who want to enter his Kingdom must take the limits off their gifts. Here is a sevenfold statement of the Law, in a form you can all remember.

" 'Be merciful that you may obtain mercy.
Forgive that it may be forgiven you.
As you do, so shall it be done to you.
As you give, so shall it be given you.
As you judge, so shall you be judged.
As you are kind, so shall you be kindly treated.
With what measure you weigh, it shall be weighed out
    to you.'

"Now as you study the temptations to which each of you is subject, you will notice two things: First, each disciple is inclined to exempt himself from Jesus' rule at the point where it is most convenient for him to do so. But it is just where the plow cuts into the soil that it makes room for the seed. And, second, each temptation is an opportunity for us to understand why there is conflict between Christ and the world, and to locate the ties that bind us most tightly to the old life. And that is just the point where repentance can save us, just the point where God's forgiveness can act to draw us near the Kingdom. The spot of greatest resistance is the spot where God is seeking to draw us into the orbit of his love."

Silvanus paused, waiting for a rejoinder, but none came. Finally Sara spoke, drawn at last from her reticence:

"These brothers are most impressed with the problem of controlling their deeds. They are incensed at the acts of others and feel they must retaliate. My trouble is in controlling my thoughts. This week my Jewish sisters have been busy with their tongues, slandering me, even before my parents. They whisper, 'Sara has become a disciple in order to throw off the veil and play fast and loose with the Gentiles.' One of them told my mother that I had actually become a prostitute. Now, I know that it is wisest to keep silent, that bitter words simply furnish food for lies to feed on. But those gossips are liars. And if it is sinful to judge them, then I am a sinner. I can't even look at one of them without saying under my breath, 'You liar.' Should I not become a liar if I failed to recognize them as such?"

"Sara, God does not forgive our sin by ignoring it. To call black white—that is not forgiveness. When Jesus was working in Galilee, the good people complained that he was associating with harlots. And doubtless some of his friends were harlots. He did not deny it. But he forgave the harlots, reminding them that God does not judge by the same labels as men. He forgave, too, their critics. Forgiveness requires that the sinner recognize her own sin; then she can forgive the sin of others. Forgiven-ness and forgiving-ness are twins. If you are not a harlot, but are called one, God knows it and judges accordingly. He will judge those who spread lies. But he also recognizes on your part the sin of resentment and judges accordingly. These are the words of our Lord:

" 'Judge not, that you may not be judged.
For as you judge others, so will God judge you.

" 'Why behold the speck in another's eye,
And forget the plank in your own?'

In your case, the plank may not be adultery, but vindictiveness or self-concern. You may not be content with God's right to judge you or to judge your slanderers. In any case, we must give our attention to the plank in our own eye. If this plank is a vicious thought, then repentance helps us to throw it out. It also helps us to kill the vengeful thought even before it is born. For when the new self comes to life in us, it begins to drive out the demons of hate. When we feel hatred leaving our hearts, we know that Christ will be able to purge out our future hates, as long as we follow his forgiveness."

"There you touch the problem that still baffles me." This was Quintus again. "So far I can't feel that confident about my ability to escape future hatred. Now in this group, with the blood of our martyrs still damp in the arena, I am able to forgive my enemies. But if, during the next two weeks, Tigellinus drags me to jail, tortures me in solitary confinement, and allows the other soldiers to spit at me while they crucify me, should I then be able to love them? I'm afraid not."

Silvanus replied soberly. "No one knows if he will remain steadfast or if he will turn coward. In the situation which you picture, it may be that I would curse the soldiers and you would bless them. Only God knows. And only he can give us the needed power. But if we should ever find ourselves in that situation I want you to remind me of this parable from Jesus:

" 'The kingdom of God is like a king who decided to settle his accounts with his servants and close the books. He called a debtor to him who owed ten million dollars. But he could not pay. So the king ordered him to be sold, with his wife and children and all his possessions, that the debt might be cleared. The servant fell on his knees and begged him, "Lord, give me more time, and I will pay every cent." Out of pity the king released him and canceled the debt.

" 'That same servant, as he was going out, met a fellow servant who owed him twenty dollars. Taking him by the throat, he said, "Pay up what you owe me." This fellow servant fell down and urged him, "Give me more time, and I will pay you!" But the man refused and threw the debtor into jail until he should pay the debt. Then the

king got wind of it, and called his servant to account:
"You wicked servant! Because you begged me, I canceled
all your debt. Should you not have had mercy on your
fellow servant as I had mercy on you?" In anger the king
turned him over to the jailers, till he should pay the ten
millions. So also my heavenly Father will do to every one
of you, if you do not forgive your brother from the heart.'

"There is one thing more before we go. We have all
been thinking of the stringency of our Master's commands.
We have stressed the penalties hanging over us when we
fail to give and forgive. And this threat is real. He who
hates his brother commits suicide; he ends the life, the
new life, which God has given him. He excludes himself
from the Kingdom of forgiveness.

"But there is a joyful promise hidden behind this austere
warning. For he who loves his enemy is actually putting on
the new self; he actually enters the road to joy and peace.
When he trudges along this road, he is happy, for he is
walking with the Messiah and all his faithful companions.
And to this company the Messiah gives this blessing:

"'Blessed are you poor, for yours is the kingdom of God.
  Blessed are you who are hungry, for you shall be satis-
      fied.
  Blessed are you who are weeping, for you shall laugh.
  Blessed are you when men hate you, ostracize you, re-
      vile you, slander you on account of the Son of man!
  Rejoice and leap for joy,
  For your reward in heaven is great;
  For so their fathers treated the prophets.'

"As we go about our work, then, let us be grateful in
every trial for the opportunity to learn the way of Christ.
Let us bless him who has forgiven us. And he will bless us.

"Blessed art thou, Lord, who dost bring us from death to
life, and from hatred to love! Amen."

CHAPTER 19

Fear and Faith

CERTAIN happenings during the next week made a deep impression on Clement's mind and established him further in his new faith. The first came on Monday. During the morning's work Sabinus visited the Esquiline construction with his clerk on a routine tour of inspection. He checked over the supplies of building materials, making out the orders for more stone, lumber, and cement. The masons were commended for their progress. Then Clement was casually drawn aside as if to receive instructions for finishing the vestibule. He sensed a special purpose in this private conversation and feared that his master was about to dismiss him because of his connection with the Church. He was, therefore, quite amazed to learn of Sabinus' actual intention.

"You said something last week that set me thinking. When I called this new movement of yours a fantastic superstition, you asked me whether I knew enough about it to support such a judgment. I must admit you hit the nail squarely on the head. Apart from the charges Tigellinus made, I know nothing about the movement. Perhaps you are more dangerous than the police suspect. In any case, it is my duty as a city commissioner to know what's going on. I have decided to investigate for myself by visiting one of your meetings. If you will tell me where you meet and when, I shall be at the next session. If your crowd is as innocent as you claim, you need not be afraid I shall turn spy. I shall come disguised, but if you should recognize me, don't let it be known."

"Agreed," replied Clement quietly. "Except for the supper which disciples share, the meetings are open to everyone, even to spies. And nothing will be altered because you are there. We come together to worship God, not to impress men. Since I may not recognize you, let me say now that you will be most welcome. Feel free to ask any questions that occur to you. None of the disciples will try to embarrass you. We gather about five o'clock, as soon as men can get there from their work." Then he explained how to reach Della's home, and added that he would tell no one of the plan.

All day the prospect tantalized Clement. Would he recognize Sabinus? Might some of the brothers offend him with their lack of good taste or their plebeian manners? Who was scheduled to speak? Where would the discussion lead, and with what results? Clement admitted to himself that he was much concerned—more so than if another freedman or slave were coming, for Sabinus was of no small prominence in Rome. He held the position of a knight, but the power of an aristocrat.

In my concern am I showing partiality forbidden to a Christian? Perhaps my interest is due to my affection for

Sabinus as an old friend of the family. Or is it due to Sabinus' power over my own fate?

The day passed slowly, for fear and hope made Clement impatient. Finally, however, the sun's shadow moved around the dial to quitting time, and he hurried home.

More than the usual number of worshipers came that evening, and the back row was filled with inquisitive visitors. Clement, now that he had been baptized, took his seat near the front. He was neither able nor inclined to scrutinize closely the faces of the strangers and he caught only a glimpse of Sabinus among them. Soon he forgot his employer's presence in his absorption in the service of adoration and thanksgiving.

Rufus was in charge. He began the service with the customary benedictions addressed to God: "Blessed art thou, O Lord . . ." There followed special praises addressed to the Master who had lifted them from despair to hope, and from fear to courage. The Scripture of the evening was selected from the second book of Moses, the familiar story of God's deliverance of Israel from Egypt through the prophet Moses.

It was a long story, and Rufus read it slowly: How God appeared to Moses and commanded him to lead his people out of slavery to a land that He promised to give them. Then came the narrative of the obstacles in fulfilling this demand: God hardened the ruler's heart, so that the Pharaoh sent his army in pursuit of the exiles. Fear-ridden and depressed, the Israelites began to rebel against Moses, who now appeared to be a treacherous leader luring them into the wilderness to perish. But God strengthened Moses' heart, and the lonely leader patiently urged the footsore and hungry people forward. Then, closely hounded by enemies, they had come to the Red Sea. Here God had caused the water to divide to let the refugees through and had then caused the water to flow back, submerging the pursuers.

Then Rufus commented vividly but briefly upon this story. He accented the fact that God's hand was behind the very hostility of the Egyptians, that he wished to test the perseverance and loyalty of his people, tempting them to reject the deliverer he had sent. He called attention to the fact that, over and over again, Israel had discovered God's power in adversities rather than in prosperities. The obvious parallels between Israel in Egypt and Christians in Rome needed no extra emphasis.

Then followed the story of Jonah. Here was a prophet who tried, out of fear and weakness, to escape an errand for which God had called him. He had taken a boat in the opposite direction. But God had used the storm and sea to cut off Jonah's escape. Finally Jonah had been willing to accept the assignment to Nineveh. Rufus painted the picture of the fearful odds against the success of the mission in Nineveh. Jonah had called these foreigners to repent, and, contrary to his expectations, God's word had been powerful enough to bring to repentance the most wicked city of the time. Again, the analogy between Nineveh and Rome was clear.

Rufus concluded with a short anecdote about an incident when the disciples of Jesus had found their courage faltering. In a burst of enthusiasm, a man had said to Jesus, "I would like to follow you wherever you go." And Jesus had discouraged his hasty decision, saying, "The foxes have dens; the birds have nests; but the Son of man has no place to sleep." Another disciple had begged, "I will follow you, Lord, but first let me go and bury my father." To this Jesus answered: "Follow me. But leave the dead to bury their own dead."

In spite of these rigorous demands, some actually did

follow Jesus. These he took with him in a boat. A storm arose, and the boat was in danger of sinking. Their Master, unconcerned over what seemed an emergency, was asleep. In terror the disciples awakened him, shouting: "Save us, Lord! We are sinking." Then came a calm answer: "Why are you so afraid? You have such little faith!" He arose and rebuked the storm, and it ceased. Then his disciples confessed: "Such a man! Even the wind and sea obey his voice!"

"It is God," commented Rufus, "who through his Messiah raises and quiets the storms that confront his followers. To you who belong to this dying world, he calls: 'Follow me. But leave the dead to bury their own dead.' To disciples who have chosen to follow, but who become alarmed by the danger, he warns, 'Why are you so afraid?' To some of us as to Jonah, that hesitant and doubting messenger, he says, 'Go to that wicked city, and cry, Repent.'"

The first moments of the period of prayer that followed were hushed. Then came short ejaculations: "Lord, I believe!" "Jesus, I would follow thee!" Then came a voice which Clement recognized as Quintus', in a prayer of gratitude for power to forgive his enemies, the other soldiers; then a woman's voice, thin and tremulous, in a petition for the emperor and his police—it was Della. Then followed others, some incoherent and brimful of emotion, others subdued and fading off into mere whispers. Silvanus offered thanks that God was able to use every calamity as a means of fulfilling his purpose. Then he began a psalm in which the others joined:

"'The Lord is my shepherd;
I shall not want.
He gives me rest in green pastures;
He leads me by quiet waters.
He restores my soul . . .'"

After they had joined in the amen, the group disbanded in silence.

By the time Clement had escaped the spell of worshiping sufficiently to look around, Sabinus was well on his way home. It was two days later that the two met again, and then Sabinus was obviously not in a mood to discuss his reactions at length.

"Perhaps you were half right, Clement," he remarked gruffly. "I called this movement a dangerous superstition. I now doubt if it is dangerous, but I still believe it is a superstition. All this about the Red Sea and Jonah and a man who controls storms . . ."

Clement was a bit stung by this, and his words were hasty. "Sir, it may be more dangerous than you fear, and less superstitious than you hope."

Sabinus checked his impulse to reply, and marched stiffly about his business.

That same evening, when Clement arrived at Della's house, Silvanus was waiting for him. The need had arisen for special couriers to be sent to another Christian group, far out on the Flaminian Way. For many years a group of slaves had been meeting in their barracks on the estate of Narcissus. At first their meetings had flourished, until several dozen of the slaves had been converted, most of whom were illiterate pagans from North Africa. Their master, a wealthy and arrogant patrician, had at first tolerated the new excitement, looking patronizingly upon their beliefs as a harmless diversion. Noticing the patient and uncomplaining faithfulness of these workers, he had even advanced a few of them to positions of importance in his household staff.

Then one day a Christian slave had run away, aided—or so Narcissus assumed—by the others. Another Christian had created a disturbance by recommending his faith to a guest of the master. And several of them had refused when guests wanted to use them in satisfying depraved lust. Moreover, the contagion of the faith had spread until Narcissus feared that it might come to include the majority of his slaves. So he had taken measures, more or less indirect at first, and then more open, to show his opposition to the group. He had demoted them to the most menial tasks. With little provocation he had ordered floggings.

During Tigellinus' purge, Narcissus had decided on further steps. Always dependent upon the emperor's patronage, he wanted to make a show of his loyalty. Too, some of the Christians were getting old, unable to work long hours. The owner, calculating that younger slaves would be more profitable if he could rid himself of those who were worn out, had given a long list to the police, who thus weeded out the oldest, among whom were the more trusted leaders.

Nor did Narcissus stop with this measure. He banned the meeting of the Christians on his property, and placed on short rations those who did not recant. Since the purge, he had legal justification for such policies, if he had needed any. As a result, the tiny cluster of disciples had been forced to meet secretly in a near-by grove. Depleted in numbers, hungry and discouraged, their will to resist was nearly exhausted. Narcissus had made it clear that none of them could expect any easier prospect until they gave up their faith.

It was from a desire to encourage these slaves that the Church in Della's house had decided to send a token of fellowship. One of the deacons had been appointed to carry food to them; and the members had been so liberal that four baskets were waiting to be carried, baskets filled with bread, beans, leeks and other food. Clement, therefore, found himself making a long trip to the northern suburbs of the city. He accompanied the deacon, himself a slave.

It was almost dark when they reached the grove on the Flaminian Way. They located the band of brothers— eleven of them there this evening. They had just finished their worship service. Quite overjoyed with the gifts and deeply moved by this expression of solidarity, they invited the two messengers to their barracks, where they broke bread together. It was a simple meal, yet one that nourished the spirit of confidence and kinship. Clement could not remember ever having experienced so intimate a comradeship formed so instantaneously among strangers. Painful memories and anxieties were expelled by a mood of good humor and even hilarity. For a time they forgot the hazards and tensions under which they lived. Clement found himself stirred by the marks of patient endurance on the faces of these slaves; they, in turn, were inspired by the hopefulness of the visitors.

When they had finished their meal, the hosts invited Clement and his companion to speak about their own experiences. The deacon began, telling the recent history of the disciples who had met in Jonas' house, of the effects of the arrests, and of the new arrangements that had been made to carry on the faith. Suddenly confronted by his first call to address a group of fellow Christians, Clement was nonplused.

What have I to give these brothers? he thought. *Here they have borne the brunt of the world's hatred for so many years, day after day, turning away from the path of compromise. And I have entered the fellowship so recently; what do I know of the reservoir of hope from which to draw?*

But he did not apologize, nor could he refuse to speak, for that would mean disappointment to these new friends.

So he began to relay to them what he could remember from the sermon of Rufus. He told the story of slavery in Egypt, the despairs of the captives, and the power of God's promise to strike off their chains. Then he gave the account of Jonah's mission to Nineveh, and of its miraculous results. From Egypt to Nineveh to Rome, he followed the progression of the divine promise, so captured by the theme that he quite forgot himself. Forgotten also was the time, and when he had finished it was very late, far too late for the two guests to return to their homes. The invitation to sleep in the barracks was gladly accepted. And after saying together the psalm about the green pastures, the quiet waters, the table in the presence of enemies, the disciples gave each other the night's blessing and went to sleep.

As Clement dropped off, his mind was filled with a strange peace. Far into the inner recesses of his mind had seeped the strength drawn from these brothers. But on the surface of his mind hovered other impressions; he could not forget the attentive hush that followed his narration of the three empires. His words seemed to have power to break through the shell to the kernel of men's minds. So diffident was Clement by nature that he was amazed at this response to his first public testimony. The second impression was even sharper. For, as the disciples were dispersing for the night, two of Narcissus' men drew him aside and volunteered confessions of guilt. One had been at the point of renouncing his faith in exchange for his owner's favor. The other had been asked by Narcissus to serve as undercover reporter on the activities of the Church, and he had almost fallen into this treachery. Both expressed their gratitude for the renewed courage which Clement's message had instilled in them.

A third incident contributed to Clement's training during this week. It was a visit to the Synagogue of the Olive Tree on the morning of the Sabbath. Several weeks had passed since he had seen Bar-Joseph, since he had moved his lodging to Della's house, and he missed the contact with this trusted friend. Too, it had been almost three weeks since he had attended a synagogue service. The double desire became almost irresistible. So, arising early, he crossed the city in time for the morning prayers. So much had happened during the short interval that he felt like a different person.

As Clement glanced over the congregation, he failed to find Bar-Joseph. He wondered what had happened to him, and decided that he must stop at his home to find if he were ill. Here and there he spotted a Jew whom he knew. And over in the women's section, he nodded to Sara. The liturgy quickly absorbed his attention, and he lost any sense of estrangement. He saw this worshiping community with new eyes, yet the sense of belonging was no weaker than it had been on the earlier occasions.

He joined in the benedictions, the Shema and the Shemoneh Esreh, and became lost in reverie. Yes, surely God was speaking to these people, even though they had not accepted his Messiah. Surely he had a hidden purpose for them, even in their rejection of Jesus as the Coming One. Would he always hide the truth about the Messiah from such saints as his father and Bar-Joseph? Would he wholly destroy this people who had kept the altar lights burning through so many dark nights? In imagination Clement saw a long procession of earlier moments in his own life, moments when God had been leading him, though by a path on which the pilgrim had not known where the next turning might take him. Is not God also leading all faithful sons of Israel, each by a different path, to be sure, but each ultimately to the same goal?

Such were his thoughts when the elder began to read from the Prophets. Here another chain of associations started, and Clement followed it with almost breathless alertness. A series of pictures began to flash upon his inner vision, as the elder read:

> " 'I am inquired of by men who did not ask for me;
> I am found by men who did not seek me;
> To a nation that was not called by my name, I said
> Behold me! Behold me!' "

Clement recalled the scene in Narcissus' barracks— slaves in immediate jeopardy, none of them Jews by birth, but all of them found by God and called to serve his name. Again he heard them repeat the psalm of the sheep and the shepherd . . .

The words of the elder droned on:

> " 'I have spread out my hands all day toward a rebellious people, that walk in a way that is not good, after their own thoughts; . . . men who say: Stand by yourself. Don't come near me, for I am holier than you.' "

Now there loomed up a picture of Bar-Joseph—kindly, weather-beaten, dependable, self-forgetful. Was such a man a rebel against God? Had he been fooled by "a way that is not good" into the position of saying, "I am holier than you"? Was this revered elder, who had dismissed Christians as covenant breakers—could he himself be a breaker of the covenant? The contradiction of the two pictures, the Christian slaves and the Jewish elder, broke into his heart and were like ropes pulling him in two directions at once.

The Scripture lesson continued:

> " 'These are like smoke in my nose,
> A fire that burns all day long.

" 'I will recompense your own iniquities
    And the iniquities of your fathers.'

"If this be God's will, to destroy his own rebellious people, toward what goal did God's hidden purpose move?
The Scripture gave an answer:

" 'As the new wine is found in the cluster,
    And one says, "Destroy it not, for a blessing is in it":
    So will I do for my servants' sakes,
    That I may not destroy them all.

" 'I will bring forth a seed from Jacob,
    From Judah an heir of my mountains;
    My chosen shall inherit it,
    My servants shall dwell there.' "

Yes, from the vine, however withered, there would be
wine. From among the rebels, however blind, there would
come servants. God would reap his harvest. A picture of
Peter, preaching on the synagogue steps, crossed the
screen of his mind . . . then a picture of Sara . . . then one
of himself, Clement. Were they part of the new wine
pressed from this cluster? Again the Scripture reading provided an answer:

" 'Thus saith the Lord God:
    Behold, my servants shall eat, but you shall be hungry;
    Behold, my servants shall drink, but you shall be thirsty;
    Behold, my servants shall rejoice, but you shall be put
        to shame;
    Behold, my servants shall sing for joy of heart, but
        you shall cry for sorrow of heart,
        and wail for vexation of spirit,
        and leave your name for a curse.' "

With a start, Clement wondered where he had heard
this promise recently. It sounded familiar; it echoed
through his mind as if he already knew it, as if he could

repeat it himself. He cast out his hooks of recollection, until suddenly one of them caught. He saw again Silvanus and the class of students on the previous Sunday. And unconsciously he began again to intone the lines which they had memorized.

> " 'Blessed are you who are hungry . . .
> Blessed are you who are weeping . . .
> Rejoice and leap for joy . . .' "

Yes, the joy which he had sensed in Peter, in Jonas, in the slaves of Narcissus—that joy was the real thing. Here were hungry folk, folk bereaved of loved ones, folk who could look forward to little but shame in the eyes of men; but to these God had begun to fulfill his promise. Suddenly other lines came crowding around this core of reminiscence:

> " 'Blessed are your eyes, for you have seen
> Things which prophets and kings long hoped to see, but
> saw not,' . . .
> Things which eye saw not, and ear heard not,
> Things which entered not into man's heart,
> Things which God prepares for those who love him."

As the joy of sudden recognition swept over him, his thoughts were confirmed by the words read by the elder:

> " 'Be glad and rejoice for ever in that which I create; for behold, I create Jerusalem a rejoicing, and her people a joy.' "

This, then, was the new creation, the new city, the new heirs of the mountains of God. Into this city he and his fellow disciples had been brought, where they could no longer hear the voice of weeping, where they were delivered from the futility of former troubles, and from the fretting of nagging fears.

The image of Peter again flashed across the screen—
Peter, confident, calm, intrepid, joyful. Then came a voice,
cutting through all his thoughts: "Who will speak for
Peter?" A shudder shook Clement. He found himself mur-
muring in desperation: "I can't do it, Lord. Not today.
Wait. Wait until I know what to say and how to speak.
Wait until Silvanus can prepare me for the task."

Then there came to him a picture of Jonah, running
from God's voice. He knew there was no escape. Although
he did not know what he would say, he knew he must
follow the example of Peter and address this congregation,
to tell them of the new city which God was even now
building.

All too quickly the service was ended. Clement pushed
his way to the porch. His knees wobbled and his voice
shook. But his eyes were held by the vision of Peter, and
he began to select the impressions which he must try to
convey to anyone who would listen.

"Sons of Israel, listen. I have been commanded to say
something to you. A few weeks ago there stood here a messenger who announced to us the news of a Messiah. . . ."
Then Clement reminded them of the central thrust of the
apostle's talk, and reviewed what had happened to him.
"Yes, he gave his testimony to Nero. But before he died, he
had picked two grapes from the cluster in this synagogue.
Those two are here this morning. And I am one.

"But before I could believe, I doubted. And my doubts
were just as strong as those which fill your minds today."

Then Clement narrated the arguments which Bar-
Joseph and his own father and he himself had used to dis-
count the apostle's warning. He told of the peace which
Della had found, the gentleness of the soldier Quintus, the
endurance of the slaves in the barracks, the blessedness of
the hungry and the persecuted.

"All this is because we have found a leader like Moses to

bring us out of slavery, a prophet like Jeremiah to call us to repentance, a king like David to restore the holy city and the Temple of God. The prophecy of Isaiah is fulfilled: 'I will create a place of joy for you, a new heaven and a new earth.'"

Finally, Clement appealed to his listeners not to judge this message hastily, not to be deceived by their own pride, not to be offended by the inclusion of Gentiles in the new city. He urged them to hear more about the Messiah, to come to the evening meeting, to see for themselves the wonders that Jesus had performed in the middle of this pagan city.

When he finished, he realized that he had spoken so rapidly and impetuously that there had been no chance for questions or argument. And he was secretly relieved to find that no one was in a mood for debate. In his concentration on his words, he had been almost unconscious of his audience, unaware of their numbers or their reactions. Now he noticed that about fifteen had heard him out, and he was grateful to notice that Sara had been among them, with three of her friends. Although the desire to run was even stronger now than at the beginning, he waited to greet her. Also he noticed that several of the listeners had lingered.

Suddenly it dawned on him that they wanted to inquire the way to Della's house. Somehow it had never occurred to him that from this audience there might be any who would actually accept the invitation. All through the address he had been impelled by a push from behind rather than a pull from in front. He had been driven by an irresistible demand rather than by expectation of results. When he realized how surprised he was at the outcome, there came to Clement the words of Jesus to his disciples in the boat: "Why are you so afraid? You have such little faith."

CHAPTER 20

Furrow's End

How blessed and wonderful are the gifts of God, dear brothers! Life in immortality, joy in righteousness, truth in boldness, faith in confidence, self-control in holiness—all these have been given to us. And if these have already been given, what more shall not await us when the Messiah returns to establish his Kingdom through all creation? Let us therefore strive to be worthy of the grace received and to watch in hope for the promise yet to be fulfilled."

It was Sunday morning again, and the six students were in their places as Silvanus began the hour of instruction. The salutation indicated the theme for his teaching: the promise of the Messiah's return and the ways for disciples to prepare for his coming. As usual, Silvanus began the discussion by pointing up the sharp contrast between the

236

two roads which men may walk, turning to Scripture for this contrast:

"'The path of the righteous is as the morning light,
That glows brighter and brighter until full day comes.
The path of the wicked is so hidden in deepening darkness,
That they cannot see the things over which they stumble.'

"All of you," he continued, "have friends who are walking blindly on the road to death." Clement thought immediately of his futile discussion with Julian. "And you, no doubt, are trying to show them the new life which Christ brings. You recognize that their present road leads only to despair, but they stubbornly refuse to admit this fact. To them we must relay the warning:

"'The Lord's day will come in the night, like a thief.
When men are saying, "We are safe and at peace,"
Then sudden destruction falls on them
Like birth pains come to a pregnant woman,
And there is no escape.'"

"Why do you say that there is no escape?" asked Clement eagerly, hoping to find an answer that might have some weight with his friend.

"Because it is a fact that their road has no real future. To be sure, they may be confident of a bright prospect. Each man has his ambitions. And each man expects to realize his ambitions, measuring his progress by the diminishing distance between himself and the goal. But the goal is futile. He may, of course, if he wants wealth, be able to get an ample supply of it. But this wealth does not bring him the inner satisfactions he expected. So, because of this disappointment, he either tries to get more wealth or he shifts his goal to something else—to popularity, let us say. But this too turns out to be empty. Then he tries another goal, and another. When he finds that life doesn't give him what he wants, he becomes more frantic or more cynical. And the more frantic or more cynical, the farther he is from any hope by which to live. So he turns to the pursuit of pleasure and drunkenness, to any means for relieving the intolerable boredom. Now how can God save such a man except by destroying the hope to which he has pegged his life? If God's will is to be fulfilled, these puny ambitions must be frustrated. And God's judgment must fall on men like lightning, because they have supposed that their false world is the only true world. And they rest in assurance that they have plenty of time to get what they want. But they haven't. Listen to Isaiah's word:

> " 'Wail, for the day of the Lord is at hand;
>   As destruction from the Almighty shall it come.

> " 'For the stars of the sky shall not give their light;
>   And the sun shall be darkened in its journey,
>   And the moon shall not cause its light to shine.

> " 'And I will punish the world for its evil.
>   I will punish the wicked for their iniquity.
>   I will cause the arrogancy of the proud to cease.
>   I will lay low the haughtiness of the terrible.' "

Clement interrupted. "But this is so difficult for men to grasp. There have been so many cries of warning, and so many alarms have failed to be carried out. There is so little in the present to justify this expectation. What shall we say when they ask us, 'When will all this take place? How soon?' "

"The same question was asked of Jesus," Silvanus answered. "And Jesus himself denied any knowledge of the

exact day and hour of destruction. But the Messiah made
known to us that these words are meant for us. Men who
are now alive must face this final testing. And Jesus was
wholly concerned, as we must be, with preparing men for
God's judgment. Of this you may be sure," Silvanus continued, "as long as men lose themselves in preoccupation
with their own ambitions, they will never be ready for
God's judgment. Only those who seek first God's Kingdom
will be ready when it comes. I recall this parable:

"'It is as when a man, traveling in another country, has
left his house to his servants, and has given an assignment to each of them. He commanded his gatekeeper:
"Watch—for you do not know when I will return. It may
be in the evening, at midnight, at dawn, or at noon."'"

"Sometimes my friends ask me another question," interjected Quintus. "They ask me where the new age is going
to appear. They hoot at the idea that it might be established in Rome. They grant that some new order might
start in a remote place like Judea. Perhaps that is one reason why the administration of Judea is so ruthless—the
vague fear that there may be a grain of truth in Jewish
hopes. Did Jesus ever answer the question, Where?"

"Yes, he gave several answers. He compared the coming
of judgment to lightning. One can't predict where lightning will strike. And when it flashes it lights up the whole
sky. He compared it to a thief. And one never knows just
when or where the thief will break into one's house and
steal all one's possessions.

"Then too he told his enemies that the Kingdom was
breaking in all around them. The enemies couldn't see it,
but Jesus and his disciples could. They recognized its coming wherever demons were cast out of people and men by
faith became well. They recognized its coming where cap-

tives of fear lost their chains. They recognized its nearness in the joy and power that enabled them to conquer temptations and to love their enemies. Each disciple knows that the Kingdom has already begun work within his own life. God's Kingdom begins to appear wherever the battle is joined between God and his enemies. We discover this battle line, not in some distant place, but here and now. And wherever we see victory in this battle, we see God's arm at work."

"But others can't see all this," protested Clement. "They think that we are talking nonsense when we speak of the Kingdom in these terms. Did Jesus not give a more convincing answer for others?"

"I recall an answer that conceals the truth in a riddle: 'Wherever the carcass is, to that spot will the vultures fly.' What does that mean? Judgment will fall wherever there is rottenness. As disciples, if we watch, we shall discover the vultures of God's judgment hovering all around us. We may not know in advance just where the vultures will swoop down, but we know that there can be no peace between God and the rebel, between the Coming One and those who say, 'We are at peace.'"

"But there are so few of us." This was Joseph. "My Jewish friends think of our number and say, 'You are just a harmless handful.' 'These disciples of Jesus,' they say, 'claim that God cares more for their wretched skins than for the whole family of Israel.' How can I answer them without seeming self-righteous, as they charge?"

"When Noah preached repentance, only a few obeyed and were saved. When God destroyed Sodom, only a few left the city and were saved. When our Messiah was asked whether many would be saved, his only answer was this: 'Strive to enter the narrow gate that leads to life.' Of the judgment, he also said:

" 'In that night two men shall be in one bed;
One shall be taken and the other left.
Two women shall be grinding at the mill;
One shall be taken and the other left.'

"Men who are content to live in darkness, thinking that
they are safe, will always be skeptical of prophets who
warn them to flee from the coming wrath. They will always laugh at the prophets and will ask, 'When? Where?
Who?' They will never be satisfied with the answers, because they are so eager to disbelieve the message. They
want the night to continue so they can still pursue private
pleasures. But soon or late, when they are most content
and least prepared, God summons them to judgment and
reveals the poverty of their souls.

"This is why the Christian must ever shout to his neighbors in the hope of saving them:

" 'Awake, you who are asleep.
Arise from your death,
And the Messiah will give you light.'

And he will find here and there a man eager to be delivered from the false road that leads to nothing. That is how
each of us was saved. So we know that it is possible for
dead men to awake. When we waken from this deadly
sleep, we find ourselves living in the dawn of the new day.
We know that God has fulfilled his promise:

" 'The people that walked in darkness
Have seen a great light:
Those who lived in the shadow of death,
On them has the light shined.' "

"Now that this has happened," Joseph inquired, "now
that night has surrendered to day, to what should we look
forward? How do we face the future?"

"Listen to the command of the apostle:

"'You are not in darkness, to be surprised by the thief;
    You are sons of light and sons of the day.
    So then let us not sleep and be drunk like those of the
        night;
    But let us watch and be sober like those of the day.'"

. Silvanus paused and asked them all to memorize this guide to behavior. Soon they were able to say it without mistake. Then Silvanus commented on this teaching, line by line. First he accented the assurance that "those of the day," because of their knowledge of the Messiah, will not be surprised by the thief. By recognizing the nearness of God's judgment they escape the fate of the sleepers. They know how sin blinds them. They know the danger of trusting in the desires and devices of their own minds. They know how temporary are the satisfactions of human ambitions. By accepting God's condemnation on their own sins, their eyes are sharpened to detect the rays of the rising sun.

Then the teacher pointed out how it had happened that they could be awakened at all, while their neighbors slept. Here Clement recognized the line of thought he had traced in Paul's letter. While we were dead, the Messiah died for us. While we were sinners, he suffered for us. He accepted judgment for us, that we too might accept God's judgment. He lives again because he lived according to God's will—and we too, through following him, share in a life that has no end.

Turning to Joseph, Silvanus continued: "You asked a moment ago what we look forward to in the future, when our Master returns. Now we don't know in detail what will happen, but we know that he will complete the work which he has begun among us. The hope of peace and joy will be fully realized; the love that is in our hearts will be extended until it includes all creation. The power of the Messiah over sin and death will be decisively demonstrated; all his enemies will be subdued. All creation will join in glorifying God, and will receive from him the things which he has prepared for those who love him. And as long as we hold fast to our faith, nothing will come between us and that perfect fellowship with God and with one another.

"The important thing for us to consider, however, is not how Christ will do this, or when it will be accomplished, but how we may become more faithful servants of the Lord. To us he gave the command to 'watch and be sober.' Now what does that mean? First of all, the watchman must stay alert and resist every tendency to go to sleep. Jesus gave us warnings against this danger:

"'No man who puts his hand to the plow and then looks back is fit to enter the kingdom of God.'

"Remember Lot's wife. When she went out from Sodom, she turned and looked backward and became a pillar of salt. If you then are double-minded doubters, you too will become a warning to all generations. If we look back from the gift of grace to the works of death, we forfeit our share in the new day of the Messiah. To drift back means that we crucify the Messiah anew, and receive even a greater condemnation than those who have never known him.

"Jesus taught that when the night ends and the day dawns, the man who is on the housetop should not even go back into his house to get his belongings. The man who is working in the field should not return home. Jesus himself refused to turn back, and demanded of his disciples: 'Leave the dead to bury their own dead.'"

"Such instructions are merely figures of speech, aren't they?" Clement asked.

"Of course they are parables," admitted his teacher. "But that is not to say that they are simply poetic exaggerations. They describe inner attitudes that are absolutely necessary. Whenever the disciple looks back with regret to the world he has left behind, he actually takes a step backward into the night."

"How, then," Clement still asked, "may we keep from looking backward? Must we not look back in order to see how far we have come?"

Silvanus continued with his explanation: "To use the parable of the plowman, the disciple keeps his plow in the furrow by fastening his eyes on the end of the furrow. He measures his position by looking ahead to the coming day. The watchman stays awake by expecting his master's return at any moment. Unless we are always ready for the Messiah, he will return and catch us napping. When we begin to slip, we must remember the promise of the prophet:

> " 'He shall come quickly and not tarry;
> The Lord shall come suddenly to his temple,
> Even the Holy One whom you expect.' "

"It seems to me," remarked Clement, "that this part of our message causes many misunderstandings. People wonder why we get so excited. They shy away from our enthusiasm as if we were jabbering maniacs. 'Our grandfathers got worked up over these expectations,' they say, 'and here we are, old and gray, and nothing has happened yet.' "

"Sometimes disciples give them an excuse for feeling that way," Silvanus answered. "I have known followers of Christ who let themselves be carried away into hysterical jabbering. I am glad that none of you is so inclined. But I have seen others so excited over the prospect of Christ's return, so absorbed in breathless waiting, that they could do no work. But this is not the kind of eagerness that Jesus wants. This is not the conduct of men who live by his light in his new day. These men forget they have already been delivered from darkness; the most important transition is over. They also forget the arduous tasks which their Master assigned to them: justice, kindness, helping anyone who needs them."

"If that is the case," returned Clement, "then how can we be eager without being overexcited? How can we remain alert for our Lord's return at any hour without becoming fanatics who see the end of the world in every comet or catastrophe?"

"There is no place for fanatics among Jesus' followers," was Silvanus' sharp and almost explosive rejoinder. "Jesus warned his disciples to be sober. He didn't want to attract hotheads who would work themselves quickly into a frenzy and then as quickly cool off. He wanted men who would carry on his work in their communities—healing, teaching, serving, wherever there is need for his love. The impatient disciple is as faithless as the drowsy one. The drowsy fellow hopes that the Lord will delay long enough for him to have a long nap. The impatient fanatic hopes that the Lord will come so soon that he won't need to work or to suffer any longer. And the hopes of both men will be dashed, because they are selfish hopes that have no place among those who seek only to do God's will. Genuine love for others never grows lazy or hysterical; and Jesus constantly shows us what genuine love means.

"God sent his Messiah to save us. But he cannot save us if we become either listless or petulant. He must test our love to see if we have received a share in Jesus' eagerness and in his patience. His love is always hopeful and always long-suffering. Hence the Messiah cannot dwell in the impatient man. But Satan loves such a man."

"Silvanus, you have me all befuddled," said Sara. "First you say we must be prepared at any hour for Jesus' return, and then you say we must be patient—as if he would not return for a long while. Does he return at different times for different disciples?"

"I too am greatly confused by this teaching," confessed Joseph. "It seems to imply that the return of Jesus depends entirely on our attitude. When we are too sleepy he will come quickly, but when we are too alert he will delay. It's strange, and I'm afraid I don't understand."

"I can appreciate these difficulties," the teacher replied quietly. "Every disciple finds himself asking such questions. And many of them cannot be answered. God does not reveal to us all the secrets of his plan. Perhaps he wishes to test our faith to see whether we will trust him as completely as Jesus trusted him.

"Jesus himself did not know the day or the hour when the Kingdom would arrive in its fullness. Yet he trusted God completely by being both alert and patient. Since our Lord was willing to accept these conditions, it is both wrong and foolish for us to chafe against them. It is wrong for us to want to know in advance more than Jesus knew about God's plan.

"This, however, does not mean that the disciple remains ignorant of the reality of the coming day. He already lives within its light. When he yields his obedience to the Messiah who died for him, he receives power which comes only from the Lord. And he knows that the Lord has power over all creation, and that he will not rest until he has brought all creation into his Kingdom.

"And when we surrender to our new King, we make his love for men our own. With him we pray, 'Thy kingdom come.' The more fully his love controls our actions, the more assured we are of his power to complete what his love has begun. Now our only obligation is to keep our hearts centered on this goal, leaving the rest in God's hands.

"What happens when we become weary or impatient? Isn't it this: Our hearts become divided? With one eye we look toward our own selfish desires, trying to keep the other eye turned forward toward the Messiah. But this double-mindedness destroys our loyalty to the Messiah. We live by faith in him, but double-mindedness kills this faith. Notice how many are the desires of men in the world. Their ambitions are unlimited, but these various motives can never be fused into a single purpose. What holds us together in the Church is the fact that all desires have been fused into one. We have but one Master, and we await his coming. Peace comes to us because we forget our former futile, clashing ambitions, because we are gripped by one all-consuming love. As the Apostle Paul used to tell us:

> " 'We rejoice in our hope of sharing God's glory.
> More than that, we rejoice in our sufferings,
> Knowing that suffering produces endurance,
> And endurance produces steadiness,
> And steadiness produces hope,
> And hope does not disappoint us,
> Because God's love has flooded our hearts
> Through the Holy Spirit which has been given us.'

"But what happens to this joy when because of our own selfishness we get impatient over the delay? Copying Paul, we may answer:

> " 'A wild enthusiasm produces hurry,
> And hurry produces impatience,
> And impatience produces petulance in suffering,
> And petulance produces self-pity,
> And self-pity produces unsteadiness,
> And unsteadiness produces vain hopes,
> And these hopes continually disappoint us,
> Because self-love has flooded our hearts
> Through the Evil One who has deceived us.'

"I must add too that impatience corrupts our fellowship. You have marveled at the miracle of our unity in Christ. Here we are: slaves, freedmen, Jews, Gentiles, men, women, young, old. Elsewhere we never experience such intimacy of understanding as in the Church. Why? For this reason: Men in the world have as many hopes as there are men, but men in the Church have but one, the hope we receive from Christ. Because we live by one promise, all other desires are included within it or forgotten. But if we should cease to press on toward the Kingdom, what then would happen to our fellowship? It would dissolve. Could Gaius and Clement agree? Could Quintus and Sara find genuine unity? No, we cease to be bound together in Christ when we cease to be ready for his return."

When Silvanus had finished, Quintus was the first to speak. "In the language of the army, could one say that God has posted us as his sentries? We have been told the secret of the strategy for the next day's battle, and have taken our stations to watch for the infiltration of the enemy. Each of us has his own sector of the front; each sector is important. The enemy waits until we get drowsy and then he strikes. To defeat him, we must stay alerted for every movement or sound. I know from experience how difficult that is—how monotonous, how nerve-racking."

"The analogy is excellent," Silvanus agreed. "You should make a parable out of your experience, Quintus. You have given a picture of watchfulness. Here is a picture of patience that our Lord painted:

" 'If a man has a servant who has been plowing, will he say to him, as soon as he has come in from the field, "Come at once and sit down at my table"? Will he not say instead: "Prepare supper for me. Serve me. After I have eaten you shall eat"? Will he thank the servant because he did what was ordered? So also with you, after you have done what is ordered, say: "We are unworthy servants. We have only done our duty." '

"You may recall the story that Rufus told last week about the storm that struck Jesus and his disciples while they were in the boat. Fear drove the disciples into frenzy, but Jesus slept on unconcerned. If we share his faith we can sleep through the storms which throw the world into hysteria. Such storms may jeopardize the world's hopes, without endangering ours at all.

"Recall, too, the story of Jesus when he was facing his death and was tempted to avoid it. Just before he was arrested, he was in a garden with his disciples. He knew that this crisis was final, for his decision would determine whether he would be obedient to God's purpose or would fail utterly. But while he was watching and praying for strength to meet the crisis, his followers, unaware that anything important was taking place, fell asleep. When he came and found them sleeping, he rebuked them: 'What! Couldn't you watch with me for a single hour?'

"So it is with us also. While the world sleeps, complacently supposing that nothing crucial is happening, we must be like sentries on the alert, watching with him, praying with him, that we too may be faithful servants. Then, whenever he comes, he *will* find us watching."

CHAPTER 21

Looking Backward

SILVANUS' instructions as to alertness and soberness had sunk deeply into Clement's consciousness. As a new disciple, he had been inspired by the pictures of the watchman waiting for the dawn and the plowman pushing patiently down his furrow, his eyes fixed on the end. These pictures fed his courage and stiffened his determination to persevere on this new road unto the day of the Lord.

But Clement's resolution was sorely tested during the week. Could he keep from looking backward at the life that he had left? The first test came when on Sunday evening he carried out his intention to visit Bar-Joseph. Yesterday, the elder's absence from the synagogue service had prevented their meeting. Today, therefore, as soon as work was over, Clement walked directly to the spacious home on the Janiculan hill.

The elder was ill, and Clement was saddened to notice how quickly his friend had lost his robust vigor. Perhaps the excitement of the arrests had drained his reserve energy. Or perhaps the long strain of caring for the refugees had fatigued him. In any case, he now appeared old and frail, not at all his usual self.

Nor was his welcome as deep and genuine as Clement had learned to expect. As Clement talked about some of the things that had happened to him since he had moved his lodgings, it became obvious that Bar-Joseph was not particularly interested. Because of this coolness, Clement brought his remarks to an awkward pause. At once Bar-Joseph began.

"They told me about your visit to the synagogue yesterday. Had I been there, I would have interrupted you."

"I'm sorry you don't approve my new faith," replied Clement in a mild and subdued tone. "Yesterday I came partly to see you and partly to worship. I had not planned to speak. But during the worship I felt a command which I could not evade. As Jonah learned, I too have learned that it is useless to flee God's errands."

"That's one thing that I can't tolerate," Bar-Joseph replied sharply. "In this new faith you so easily imagine yourselves as prophets and class yourselves with the great heroes of Israel. Our people have always attracted self-appointed prophets, as a horse attracts flies. They buzz around and sting us, but each fly dies in a day or so. You're too young, Clement, to assume authority for chiding and condemning our people. You may talk of meekness, but you act like a spoiled child."

Clement was stunned by both words and tone, and he tried to speak respectfully: "Sir, your attitude seems to have changed. You have always been sympathetic and considerate. Why have you suddenly become so bitter? I had hoped that you and I might remain close even though God has called us to follow different paths."

The elder hardly stopped to weigh his words. "At first I thought this was an innocent infatuation which would soon pass. Since you had just come from the country I supposed it was natural for you to be attracted to strange, new sects. But I was confident you would have enough sense to know how absurd this Christian message is. Now that you have spoken publicly, I know that you have committed yourself too far to retreat. You have destroyed my confidence in you. More than that, by your impudence yesterday, in trying to lure others away from our synagogue, you have openly defied the leaders of your people. What can we do but resist you? Your father is as alarmed as I am by your treachery. He wrote me to ask me to dissuade you. But what is there that I can do now? And what am I to write to him? Is this the way you show your gratitude for my hospitality?"

"I understand your feelings." Clement tried to hide his distress. "But can't you write my father that I am sincere in my loyalty to God? However wrongheaded I may be, I am trying to follow the path of duty. Doesn't our goal remain the same—the desire for God's Kingdom? It has not been easy for me to follow the call of the Messiah, but now I can never turn back. [The vision of the plowman crossed his mind.] Now I know that Jesus *is* the King whom Israel has long expected."

"These very words prove how impossible it is for us to agree." The elder was near the edge of his temper. "When you claim for Jesus the approval of God, and proclaim him as the King of Israel, what is left for us but to bar you from our meetings? If you are conscience-bound to follow him, we are conscience-bound to oppose you in the name of the God of Abraham, Isaac, and Jacob. What peace can there be between us?"

Both men saw that it was useless to talk longer. And both were suffering from the inner tension between the wish to remain friends and the compulsion to be loyal to their differing duties. Both were therefore relieved when Clement excused himself as courteously as he could. As he left, Bar-Joseph gave him a letter from his father.

Clement did not immediately open the letter because the wound that Bar-Joseph had inflicted was too deep and too fresh. As he walked slowly toward Della's home, he tried to think of some healing element in the situation. Was he himself now one of these disciples who must "leave the dead to bury the dead"? Or could there still be a road to a reconciliation? He recalled what Silvanus had said about the fellowship created by a common goal. Would his own father and his Jewish friends ever realize that Christians too were pursuing the selfsame promise? Or was it in fact the same promise? Did the fellowship of Christians automatically exclude all who could not share their hope?

Whatever the answer, Clement suddenly realized how much he needed the other disciples if he were to face without fear this separation from his own kin. He speeded up his steps and arrived at Della's home in time to share the evening meal with the disciples.

The supper and the words of Jesus repeated by Silvanus served to soothe the smart of Bar-Joseph's antagonism. They served also to prepare Clement for reading his father's letter. He knew in advance what it was likely to say. As soon as possible, he excused himself and went to his room.

❖   ❖   ❖

MATTATHIAS TO HIS SON CLEMENT, GREETING:

Your letter greatly disturbed us. I regret that I have not been able sooner to find a messenger whom I could trust with this answer. Naturally, we are worried over your safety. Had we known how dangerous was the situation in Rome, we would never have allowed you to leave here in the first place.

Things at home are quiet; here there would be no danger from political authorities. We fear that even now you may have been arrested. Your mother is more alarmed than I, and I console her by saying that you can hardly be convicted for starting a fire which happened two months or more before your trip to Rome.

If Sabinus is willing, come home immediately. If he is not, do not endanger yourself by keeping your present company. We can hardly believe that in this matter you would neither follow Bar-Joseph's counsel nor consult us before taking so hazardous a step. Why should you so recklessly join in supporting a movement that is rejected by both synagogue and state?

At this distance we cannot force you to come home. Nor can we prevent you from continuing this sudden infatuation. But please be considerate enough to write to us immediately that you are well, and assure us that you will go no farther in your support of this sect. Because any letter may get into the wrong hands, I have been forced to guard my statements, but you should be able to understand our wishes. We count on you to obey us as you have always obeyed us in the past.

❈　　　❈　　　❈

So this is where the road turns, thought Clement. *I hardly imagined, when Silvanus was talking about the night and the day, that actually I might have to break with both the synagogue and my home.*

Clement recalled the feeling of togetherness that had permeated the Church in Della's house and the Church at Narcissus' estate. *Nothing like that ever happened to me before,* he thought. *Yet to be turned out of home and synagogue would be a bitter blow. Will God require me to surrender so much?* Before Clement's eyes there came pictures of the supper in Della's home and another in his father's. *Must I choose to eat at one and not at the other?*

His thoughts were broken by Silvanus, who entered the room which they were now sharing. Both were tired, and Clement hesitated to trouble the teacher. Nevertheless, he handed him the letter without comment, and Silvanus read it carefully. Then Clement reported briefly on his interview with Bar-Joseph. Silvanus, to Clement's astonishment, said very little.

"Every disciple must bear his own burden. You must decide for yourself. I shall pray that God may show you the way. Don't be anxious, but be grateful that even this situation is an opportunity for serving the Master."

Clement resented such a curt dismissal of an acute problem. Secretly he had hoped that Silvanus would be both impressed and upset by this difficulty. It was a bit unnerving to have him treat it so casually.

During the week, Julian and Clement had several opportunities for short chats. Although the demands of their work kept them from pursuing any single topic to its end, they carried on a running conversation dealing with various matters. Clement made no mention of his quarrel with Bar-Joseph or his father's letter. As the days proceeded, Clement became aware that something was also happening to his friendship with Julian. They were as cordial to each other as ever, and they continued to work well together. Yet underneath the work and speech Clement sensed a growing chasm. The hidden roots of their thinking seemed to feed in different soils. They seemed not to need each other. At odd moments during the days Clement asked himself why this should be.

Was it perhaps because one mind was carefree while the other was preoccupied? On occasion, Julian, with a touch of irony, suggested that Clement was too intent upon his private problems of belief. Clement, in rejoinder,

accused his friend of being too lighthearted and noncha-
lant in dealing with problems of such importance. Julian
feared that his friend's faith was making him dogmatic
and intolerant. Clement began to wonder if Julian's bland
tolerance was the cloak for cynical indifference. Julian
would listen patiently to Clement's talk about his new convictions and would smile in a fashion that might signify
secret ridicule or carefully guarded sympathy—Clement
could not be sure which.

He tolerates my faith, he thought. *Is it the principle of
'live and let live,' or is he more interested than he cares to
show?*

In his heart Clement knew that Julian was not taking
seriously the problems which to him had become central,
and he was hurt to discover that the bonds which had developed during many years of teamwork were not strong
enough to bridge this new gulf. On the other hand, he was
made aware of the fact that he was no longer so dependent
upon his friend. Julian's place was being taken by the fellowship of disciples. Yet Clement felt close to Silvanus
and Quintus and Sara in a way entirely different from his
feeling for Julian. The new circle had been drawn together
by different forces. It had been woven by threads of common loyalty to a single Master. And because this Master
was invisible, their life with one another was somehow
on a deeper level. Somehow the new friendships had been
created *for* them, and were not based on mutual attraction
or congeniality.

Clement and Julian were still congenial in temperament.
They were still linked together by a common background,
made rich by mutual memories. They enjoyed the work on
the house. But suddenly there appeared to be no future
which they could share. As long as they limited conversation to the past and to their work, everything went well.

But the moment either would mention what lay ahead, both became uncomfortable, and their words would be edged with caution and even friction.

Each day made it clearer that the tone and color of their friendship had shifted. And Clement kept fearing that someday the inner tension would erupt into open antagonism. In the morning he would come to work, elated by some new discovery in his new world. But by evening he would return home with his nerves frayed. When he kept silent about his faith he felt the twist of a conscience that accused him of being afraid to speak. But whenever he mentioned Jesus to Julian, the chasm between them grew, and his conscience became sore. He wanted his friend to discover and share the new faith, for he realized that it could enable them to overcome the barriers that had always separated them—a Jew and a Gentile. But Julian stubbornly kept on scoffing at Clement's convictions.

"You worry too much about the future," Julian said one day at lunch. "You did even as a Jew; now as a Christian your ailment is worse. You drive men into a frenzy with your shouts that the end of the world is at hand." All this was in a joking tone, yet it was barbed too.

"Perhaps you're right," began Clement. "As a Jew I was taught to look forward to the coming of God's Kingdom. Now this eagerness is intensified because I know who the King will be. But what would Seneca, your wise man, do? Ignore the future completely?"

"Not at all," Julian countered easily. "It is simply a question of which goal one seeks. According to Seneca, every man travels a road that has an end, but most men lose their way on blind detours."

"Then why do you complain that I worry too much over finding the true end? Isn't it a matter of life and death?"

"You don't spend too much energy. But all energy spent in walking in the wrong direction is wasted."

"Bravo! You talk almost like a Christian."

"Don't cheer too soon," smiled Julian. "Seneca would say that to worry about tomorrow is a sheer waste of energy that prevents a man from finding the right road today. Men do infinite damage to themselves by these unceasing anxieties about tomorrow."

"Wherein lies the damage?"

"It is always today for the wise man. The foolish man tries to escape today by dreaming of a better day somewhere in the future. He uses today simply to collect the tools he thinks he will need tomorrow. But tomorrow never comes. The good life which we postpone until tomorrow always passes us by, as if it belonged to someone else. As far as we are concerned, it vanishes while we waste our time preparing for it. Then we die before we know how to use the present moment."

"Again you sound almost like a Christian," remarked Clement. "The disciple of Jesus is not anxious about the morrow but tries to be faithful today. You say that if a man forgets tomorrow he will make the best use of today. But we know that a man uses the present rightly only when he is alert, ready at any hour to face the Messiah who will test his loyalty."

Their work now took the two disputants to opposite corners of the structure. Like boxers between rounds, they began to marshal their reserves for the next tiff. Soon the interchange began again.

"Do you really believe," Julian gave the first thrust, "that a man can find happiness only if he expects Jesus to return soon to transform the whole universe?" He had spent some time in sharpening this question to make an affirmative answer seem absurd.

Clement thought for a moment. "I'm not sure what you mean by happiness. Christians do not often use the word. It's a tricky one, and it seems to imply that a man can tell in advance what happiness will mean to him. We believe that God creates every man for a purpose, and that this purpose is fulfilled only when man finds his place in God's Kingdom. I am happier now than I had ever supposed was possible. In fact, two months ago I didn't know that such happiness existed. And this is only an advance installment of a far greater blessedness when Jesus has completed his work of establishing God's Kingdom."

"How do you know that the king will return? What if he doesn't come? Won't that be a pleasant shock for you?" Now the note of derision was unmistakable.

"If Jesus is not the King, then of course we are to be pitied. But because he is alive now we know that he will come and fulfill his promises to us. We know that our Master will not be content until the whole world shares the joys of his Kingdom. And when he comes, what will *you* say to him then? Will you be so . . ." Clement could not find the right word. He was tempted to use "smug," "complacent," "proud"—but all of them were too dangerous. Julian, however, did not wait to hear the epithet.

"I would choose to trust something that keeps its pledges. The right philosophy not only promises happiness, but also produces its proof. The Stoic knows that nothing will happen tomorrow that does not happen every day. Death is not a future catastrophe, but actually we die every day, a bit at a time. The Stoic does not cling to life like a man carried down stream by a rushing torrent. He does not clutch at the briers and rocks along the bank, nor try to retrieve life by holding on to each day's pleasures and desires. He simply accepts the stream and accepts the fact that it will end. This frees his reason so that he can find contentment and happiness today, a happiness that makes him independent of death and all disaster."

"You talk as if you had memorized your teacher's books. Is this the philosophy you talk or the way you live? Are you really as happy as you claim?" There was an ironic sting in Clement's question, which he regretted as soon as the words were out.

"No, I can't live up to the Stoic ideal," Julian admitted. "But it seems to me to be the most practical outlook in these chaotic times. And it is a thousand times more realistic than your idle dreams of coming bliss."

"Even if your road leads nowhere? Even if nothing results but a transient feeling of happiness today? It seems to me that by claiming to be happy today you are hiding from yourself the fact that deep in your heart is a terrible unhappiness and aloneness. You despair of finding any firm fellowship. You despair of the future. It is as empty as the present. So you make yourself believe that you are happy with the world as it is. I'm sure I could never find happiness along that road." Again their work separated them before Julian could reply. Sabinus sent Clement on an errand to the warehouse and he was gone the rest of the afternoon. It was a good thing, for the two tempers were hot enough to flare into angry words which both would have regretted.

During the evening Clement kept thinking about this disturbing development in their friendship. He feared that their old congeniality was gone forever unless they could find some solution to the conflict. And he realized how thin the chance was for any real agreement.

He is so certain of himself, of his happiness, of his readiness to meet any disaster. What lies underneath this certainty? Is he hiding a dread of insecurity by this proud independence? No matter what the reason may be, I'll

*never win him over so long as he thinks my faith makes me
fearful of tomorrow.*

The next day Clement began to follow a different line.
"You seem to feel, Julian, that Christians are a bunch of
cowards who are so afraid of death that they are willing
to believe anything. You would be surprised to hear them
talk about death. They mention it as naturally as they
mention going to sleep. According to Jesus, each disciple
must learn to die daily, as you said the philosopher must.
Over and over again he must learn how to die. Many of my
brothers have actually conquered the fear of death."

Then he told a bit of the story of Jonas and Della, of
Narcissus' slaves and the apostles. "You claim that our
talk about coming judgment feeds man's terrors; but actually it seems to subdue them. Do you think Seneca could
die as calmly as you saw those Christians die?"

"One can't predict about Seneca, or about anyone, for
that matter. But unless a man is happy today, under whatever adversities, he will not be happy tomorrow. If the
loss of wealth or friends or life would make me sad today,
then that loss would make me sad tomorrow. One thing
is sure—sooner or later death deprives us of everything
that we possess except the wise mind that enables us to
face all loss with poise."

"Then you don't anticipate anything new tomorrow?"

"No. All moments of time drop into the same bucket. Oh,
of course, the stage scenery will be shifted! And the actors
may go through a different set of motions. But the goal of
happiness and the conditions for attaining it do not
change."

"Assuming that all this is true," Clement replied in a
reflective rather than an argumentative mood, "what actually happens to the wise man? He achieves happiness
and peace in his own mind. But what happens to that

mind? Does it disappear? How does the wise man help other men? Does he ever find a home in a community of minds?"

"I'm not sure what Seneca would say," was Julian's unruffled answer. "The mind of the wise man becomes Godlike. It becomes like that of the other wise men in world history. Perhaps that is all we know or can know. But, however that may be, it doesn't affect the laws of happiness now. What does Silvanus say?"

"He says that the man who dies daily by serving God enters a new world. He loves all other men, and through his love God is creating a new city in which these men become citizens. How I wish you would come with me some time to meet these citizens! You would not find men driven by fears. You would find men alive with joy."

"Some evening I shall go with you," agreed Julian. "But don't count on my being impressed. A joy that is based on the future is too flimsy for me to rely on."

The shift from heated argument to more tolerant exploration made Clement bold. "You know, Julian, there is one point in which we are very different. We're good friends, and I hope nothing undermines our friendship. But my affection for you makes me more eager for you to become a Christian, while you seem quite unconcerned about whether or not I become a Stoic. Why is this?"

"It does matter to me what happens to you. But that probably means that I am not a good Stoic. Seneca teaches us to be true to our friends, but he warns us not to let our friendship jeopardize our independence. To fret about a friend's safety destroys one's own peace, and, besides, it is foolish, because the friend should also be indifferent to his own safety."

"Seneca's road seems to be a one-man road," mused Clement, as much to himself as to Julian. "He would hardly join a Church in which men carry one another's burdens and are ready to die for one another."

"The more people one allows to enter the citadel of the soul, the more difficult it is to defend that fortress. If I begin to worry about one man, I am likely to worry about all men. Then where is my peace of mind? Gone like smoke. I have allowed my affections to dissolve my reason. For surely it is not rational to forget myself in this way. A diseased mind remains diseased. And if one mind is diseased, it cannot bring health to other minds. Worrying about others is like worrying about the future. Your worry keeps expanding toward infinity, and happiness is reduced to nothing."

"In a sense the disciples might appeal to Seneca," replied Clement. "They insist that every man must stand before God and make his decision alone. No matter how many friends and relatives oppose him, he must be ready to leave them behind. Jesus said, 'He who loves father and mother more than me is not worthy of me.' Yet because our Messiah died to save others, because he died to create a new community, because he died to bring the future near to men, every disciple must take up the same load. Strange as it may seem to you, this load does not increase anxiety. It does not make blessedness more remote."

"How can that be?" Julian was still unconvinced. "I've got to be shown before I believe that a mind can be happy when it is always fretting about the future, always trying to convert men and failing, and always weeping over the sins and sorrows of the world."

"All I can say is this: Come and talk with those who are better disciples than I am. They are eager for the future without being afraid. They accept as their own the sin of all men without being less joyful. They love one another, and this love produces peace.

"Maybe I can describe the difference between your philosophy and my Master. Seneca looks at the stream of time and says: 'Rise above it. Conquer it. The stream itself leads nowhere!' Jesus steps into the stream of time and accepts all its hazards and its defeats. He makes us realize that we belong in the stream, and that it is carrying us toward God's ocean, where life is free and full. He says: 'Come, dive fearlessly into the water; love creation and suffer with it, just as God loves it and suffers with it. That is the way to know God.'"

"No, Clement," Julian replied coolly. "That doesn't make sense and I don't believe it ever will. But, to please you, one night next week I shall come to your assembly. Don't expect, though, that you will convert me. I'm farther than ever from your faith."

CHAPTER 22

Tests of Love

BLESSED be God, who has poured his love into our
hearts through the Holy Spirit which he has given
to us.

> "Love binds us to God;
> Love covers a multitude of sins;
> Love bears all things,
> Is long-suffering in all things.
> There is nothing vulgar in love,
> Neither jealousy nor competition.
> By love, the elect of God are made perfect;
> Without love nothing is pleasing to God.
> In love the Lord accepted us;
> Because of love, the Messiah died for us.
> Of love's perfectness there is no telling.

"Let us pray, therefore, that we may be kept by love
and be found in it. All the generations from Adam un-

til today have passed away, but those who have been perfected in love live in the abode of the godly. And they will be made manifest when the Kingdom of God visits us."

The teacher's customary salutation pushed Clement's thoughts back to the earlier discussion with Julian. *No Stoic could talk like that about love,* he thought. *To Julian, a man must first of all seek independence, and he jeopardizes this independence whenever he gets too concerned about the needs of other men. Silvanus teaches the opposite. Jesus loved every man so much that he died for him, and he requires every disciple to live in perfect love. In love he must be willing to suffer for all, and unless he does so he cannot know God. It's not surprising that Julian is so hostile.*

When the teacher gave him an opportunity, Clement related to the class the story of his bout with Julian and asked Silvanus to direct his teaching to the objections a Stoic would raise. Just how does the Messiah's love free one from anxiety? How can one love men without losing one's happiness over their misfortunes?

"Picture Jesus on the cross," began Silvanus. "There he shows how much he was concerned for men. Yet this concern never made him alarmed; even when men were torturing him, he looked forward in perfect confidence. He knew that God is able to redeem men only by a love that suffers for them. He was thus protected from fear of what might happen to him. His love for men made him perfectly willing to accept their hatred; his love for God made him perfectly confident that God would fulfill his promise. Thus he was as free as the Stoic ever hopes to become."

Clement could follow this. But he could also see how Julian would react. "But what if God doesn't fulfill his promise? Then what would happen to this freedom? My Stoic friend insists that if we base our freedom upon this hope of the Kingdom, then when our hope cracks, our freedom and independence are destroyed. He thinks it is absurd to base our happiness upon so vague a hope."

"Yes, in a sense he is completely right," was the teacher's reply. "If God's promise is false, then everything we do is futile. The moment we doubt God's power to fulfill the work that he has begun, that moment we lose our freedom. We get alarmed about our own fate. We stop loving our enemies. We cut our responsibilities to our brothers. And we try frantically to save ourselves by some other avenue than a search for the Kingdom.

"That is why a strong faith in Jesus as God's Son is necessary for us. To call Jesus Messiah means that we know that in him God is already fulfilling his promise. To call Jesus Messiah means that we follow his road as the only road into God's Kingdom. And that means that we seek to make our love as strong as his—or, rather, we seek to let his powerful love enter our lives and replace our weak love. To be as free as Jesus was, we must trust God as fully as Jesus did on the cross. And to trust God, we must love men as wholeheartedly as he did, regardless of the cost.

"When the Messiah's love enters us, we are made patient; when we say no to his love, then our self-concern makes us impatient. When we forget his sacrifices, or refuse to share them, then we begin to complain that God is requiring too much of us. Our courage vanishes, we become anxious, we worry about death; in short, we have lost our freedom and our peace. Listen to the word of Jesus himself:

> "'Do not worry over your life, what you shall eat,
>   Or over your body, what you shall wear.

" 'Look at the birds: they do not plant or harvest,
And yet God feeds them.
Look at the wild flowers: they neither work nor weave,
And yet God clothes them.

" 'Do not worry, saying, What shall we eat?
Or, What shall we wear?
Your heavenly Father knows what you need.
But seek first his kingdom and his righteous will,
And all these things will become yours also.' "

"But," interjected Joseph, "how may we know that he will give us everything we need, as long as the Kingdom is yet to come? When we are hungry, does he nourish us only with promises of some intangible food?"

"Your very question assumes that you do not place the Kingdom first and all other things second. How can God fulfill his promise until we serve him with our whole heart? Did not the Messiah love God with his whole heart? And did God not give to him the Kingdom, with whatever else he needed? He was hungry and homeless, despised and betrayed. Yet he gave us this pledge: 'Seek first the kingdom and everything else will be given.' If you want easier terms, perhaps it is Satan's kingdom that you seek.

"Suppose that we complained about our sacrifices and asked God to make our road easier, what sort of love would he be showing if he suddenly gave us all we asked for? If he gave in to our cowardice by dealing out a rich payment just in order to keep us loyal, he would be training us in barter and not in love. Remember what God required of Jesus. Only when a man's love is proved by perfect trust is he worthy to enter the Kingdom of God's love. God deals with each of us according to his faith."

"I think Seneca would agree," remarked Clement, "on surrendering wealth and food and friends and honor. He makes all these secondary to the primary goal of happiness and poise."

"But notice what he places first," replied the teacher. "Does he not place self first? It is *my* virtue, *my* reason, *my* happiness, *my* independence, for which Seneca demands the surrender of everything else. Jesus required that we deny our *selves* if we would enter God's Kingdom.

"Hear this parable:

" 'The kingdom of God is like a merchant in search of fine pearls, who, on finding one pearl of great value, went and sold all that he had and bought it.'

"But the devil is a merchant who wants to make us cautious bargainers. Whenever the price begins to pinch, then he plants the seeds of distrust. When Caesar threatens my body, Satan begins to whisper, 'This is too much to pay for an uncertain goal.' When hunger threatens, Satan says, 'Starvation is too high a price.' When a coveted honor is within my grasp, he plants the impulse, 'This is worth more than anything God can produce.' A good bargainer, the devil makes his kingdom very attractive. But if his kingdom is really the greatest evil, then even the smallest coin is too much to pay. And if God's Kingdom is the greatest good, all the money in the world is worth nothing in comparison. If the Kingdom is for us of priceless value, then any sacrifice becomes an occasion of joy, since it makes us an heir of the Kingdom."

Clement had been trying for some time to interrupt, to turn the conversation in the direction of meeting the Stoic arguments. "Let us suppose," he now said, "that a man today decides to pay this price for being included in God's Kingdom. What will prevent him from selling his legacy tomorrow at half price?

"What would the Stoic offer as a safeguard that tomorrow he will not lose his independence and serenity?"

"He would say that a man must study philosophy and thus learn how to train his reason and subdue his passions."

"Our protection against the future is very different. One safeguard we have is prayer. This is what Jesus taught:

> "'Ask, and it will be given you;
> Seek, and you will find;
> Knock, and it will be opened to you.
>
> "'For every one who seeks receives,
> And he who seeks finds,
> And to him who knocks it will be opened.'

In prayer the Christian asks, first of all, 'Thy will be done.' He may ask for bread, but in so doing he says, 'Nevertheless, not my will but thine be done.' He thus places himself wholly within the care of God, as naturally and simply as the birds and flowers do. He is grateful for everything as a gift from God. He trusts that God is able to do whatever is most desirable for his sons. As long as he does this, selfish fears are unable to get a foothold in his heart.

"A second safeguard against losing our morale is joy. When one surrenders his life to the Messiah, he enters the family of Jesus, and shares his joy. This joy is so glorious that he forgets whatever he has sacrificed to win it. And where this joy is found, Satan finds his weapons useless. He can drive a wedge in our defenses only when he finds us stingily counting the cost, weeping over our losses, shuddering over what may come tomorrow. But when he finds us steadfast in prayer, rejoicing in tribulation, and self-forgetful in love, he puts away his weapons until we give him a more favorable opening."

Joseph now spoke. "I seem to be chosen as the devil's advocate, but my contacts in the business world force me to measure values and estimate costs. Philosophic abstractions don't count with businessmen. Must we not admit that God's gifts are intangible, and that his reward is postponed to some imaginary future? If the Kingdom is a pearl, then it is not a pearl that we can hold in our hands now."

"Yes, this argument of the devil has enough truth in it to serve his purposes well. It is true that ours is a spiritual treasure which is hidden in God's hands and we await eagerly the time when it will be fully placed in our hands. Why, then, does God call us to sacrifice the tangible for the intangible, the present for the future? Is it not to test our love, to find if it be genuine? Love is not genuine if we must always see the person we love. Trust is not genuine if we must first eliminate all grounds for doubt.

"But this does not mean that God's rewards are hidden completely or postponed entirely. His love is ours now; the joy which it produces is ours now. We seek a city that is to come, but our hearts, in seeking it, already dwell within its walls. When the Messiah returns, our joy will simply be made perfect, because God's love, which has produced that joy, will be the power which rules that city. Listen to Jesus' assurance:

" 'Nothing is covered up that will not be revealed,
Nothing is hidden that will not be made public, . . .
What you say in the night will be heard in the day,
What you whisper in the ear will be shouted from the
     housetops.'

"Knowing, too, how severely we should be tempted by the apparent triumph of evil and by the insecurity of our life, he told us how dependable is God's love:

" 'Are not two sparrows sold for a penny?
Not one of them falls without your Father.
So too the hairs of your head are all numbered,
For you are more valuable than many sparrows.'

" 'What man among you will give his son a stone when he
asks for a loaf?
Or will give him a serpent when he asks for a fish?
If you, who are evil, are eager to give good gifts to your
children,
How much more will your Father give good things to
those who ask him?'

"This, then, is the basis of our confidence, Joseph. We trust the Father of our Lord because he has demonstrated his love for us. His Kingdom is invisible, to be sure, but love makes it visible.

"Now consider for a moment, Joseph, what would happen if God's rewards were as tangible as you suggest. Suppose that this treasure, of which Jesus speaks, were an earthly treasure. Then it would be as perishable as everything else in this corrupt order. To be imperishable, it must be heavenly. That is why our Lord commanded his servants:

" 'Do not store up treasures for yourselves on earth,
There moth and rust eat them,
There thieves break through and steal them.

" 'But store up treasures for yourselves in heaven.
There neither moth nor rust eat them,
There thieves do not break through and steal them.
Where your treasure is, there also will your heart be.'

"As long as our love is genuine, just so long is this heavenly treasure absolutely safe. The instant our love becomes false, that instant moth and rust begin to eat away at our inheritance. The disturbing thing about moths is that they work so craftily; one does not know that his garment is ruined until it is too late. A man sleeps soundly, thinking that his savings are safe, and wakens to find that a thief has stolen them. So it is with all earthly securities."

"You say that our reward is safe as long as our love is like Christ's," remarked Clement. "But how are we to know that our love is genuine and not false? Each of us is inclined to suppose that his own love is genuine. But may we simply be fooling ourselves? I am much more ready to doubt Joseph's love than my own. But actually mine may be weaker. If our future is only as safe as our love is genuine, how can we know the purity of our love?"

Silvanus answered directly. "I can speak of two tests. Both are suggested by our Lord. One is to judge by the cost; the other, by the fruits. We have already spoken of testing by cost. If one is willing to give a tenth but not a half of his wealth, or a half but not the whole of it, does he actually love God with his whole strength?

"'No man can serve two masters;
Either he will hate the one and love the other,
Or he will hold to the one and despise the other.
You cannot serve God and Mammon.'

Or, if one is willing to leave a few of his friends, but not all of them, or to leave his parents but not his children, does he love God with his whole heart?

"'He who loves his parents more than me
Is not worthy of me;
He who loves his children more than me
Is not worthy of me;
He who does not follow me by bearing his own cross
Is not worthy of me.'

If one is willing to disobey the magistrate but not the governor, or the governor but not the emperor, does he fear God with his whole soul? Again Jesus said:

" 'Fear not him who is able to destroy the body,
  And can do nothing more than that;
  Fear him who is able to destroy both body and soul,
  So that the ruin is total and eternal.'

In all these cases the principle holds: according to your love shall it be done unto you.

"When you need an example of this love in operation, consider the Messiah, who proved by his deeds that he loved his Father and his neighbor with his whole heart, his whole soul, his whole strength, his whole mind. This, Clement, is the first way by which to test the genuineness of love: its cost. Such a test, of course, does not enable you to judge other disciples as you hinted when you compared yourself with Joseph. Only the lover can say how much he is willing to give to his beloved.

"I mentioned a second test: the fruit of love. And in understanding this we need to begin with Jesus' own instructions:

" 'Do men gather grapes from thorns?
  Do they gather figs from thistles?
  A good tree cannot produce evil fruit,
  Nor can an evil tree produce good fruit.'

" 'A good man from the treasure of his heart produces
      good;
  An evil man from the treasure of his heart produces evil.
  Each tree is known by its own fruit.'

"You still haven't told us how to tell good fruit from evil," Clement reminded the teacher, somewhat nettled by the abstractness of these general statements.

"First, let us apply the test to anger. Our Lord said:

" 'Long ago it was said: You shall not kill. Whoever kills will be in danger of judgment. But I say to you: You shall not be angry. Whoever is angry will be in danger of judgment.' "

Sara broke in impetuously: "It's unfair to judge anger so harshly. Who doesn't give way to anger? Aren't we all lost, if this be final law?"

"Ah, yes, all that is true! But remember, we are not discussing what we do—but what genuine love does. Is it unfair to judge hatred as an absence of love? Every action is the fruit of some seed of desire planted in our heart. And from what desire does hatred spring? From the seed of God's desire or ours? From the seed of Christ's love or ours? This seed of hatred can produce only more hatred. Every tree which God does not plant will be rooted up.

"The difficulty you speak of, Sara, is real because we are unable to reduce this standard to external measurement. We cannot detect the source of hatred nor inflict the penalty. But He who knows our hearts can detect the seed and destroy the tree. Should not the One who plants love be able to determine when that seed is producing fruit? Should he not have the power to reject false love? How fortunate for us that in the Messiah he has revealed to us the character of true love!

"Now let us apply this principle to another sphere. Our Lord taught thus:

" 'Long ago it was said, Thou shalt not commit adultery. But I say to you, Every man who lusts after a woman has already committed adultery in his heart.'

Here again it is the seed of desire that determines what the fruit will be. Evil desire leads to lustful eyes and suggestive words. And these reveal the character of the heart. And, like every desire, this desire is subject to the judgment of the Messiah, unfailing and final. A man seeks a woman. But he wants her for himself. This is self-love, not true love. This tree too God cuts down and burns. And from that fire there is no escape.

"Examples can be found anywhere—wherever man expresses his inner inclination. Think of our common habit of trying to prove our honesty by taking an oath. Of this practice, our Lord said:

> " 'Don't swear at all, either by heaven or by earth, but make your *yes* mean *yes,* and your *no* mean *no;* otherwise you will be condemned.'

To use oaths to support our words implies a treacherous and divided heart. It implies that on other occasions we are prone to lie, if we can get away with it. In effect, I say: 'Keep your eye on me. I really want to deceive you, but this oath will protect you this time.' But why the temptation to lie? If our mind were united, our desire single, our steps directed toward only one goal, should we be inclined to deceive others? God knows both the desire and the word. Where the two are not the same, he judges accordingly. It does not help us to swear when God is present.

> " 'The lamp of the body is the eye.
> If your eye is sound, your whole body is lighted;
> If your eye is evil, your whole body is darkened.'

Since God has planted the seed of love in our hearts, we cannot hide from him whether our love is sincere or not."

"Teacher," interrupted Clement, "I think you still miss my point. I am completely convinced that God can tell when we love him and when we do not. I agree fully that his punishment is perfect and final. But the problem of the individual Christian remains: How can I be confident of the genuineness of my own commitment? I haven't been forced to make so great sacrifices as other disciples. It may be that in the next weeks I shall have to make a larger sacrifice. Perhaps I shan't love God as sincerely as I think."

"Our hearts are infinitely deceitful," continued Silvanus, nodding to Clement in assurance that he would come to his point. "You mention the sacrifices that we make for the sake of Christ. Even in making sacrifices, we may be serving other desires than God's. In giving alms, for example, a double desire may give us a double eye. Notice how Jesus taught us to give alms:

> " 'When you give alms, do not blow a horn before you in the synagogue and on the street, as the hypocrites do, that they may win men's praises. I assure you they have their reward. But when you give alms, do not let your left hand know what your right hand is doing, that your alms may be kept secret. Then your Father who sees in secret will reward you.'

You see how deeply this test goes. If I have one eye directed toward what men think of me, or even if I measure with pleasure my own unselfishness, then evil desire crowds out good desire. I exchange a reward of self-praise for the reward from God. Isn't this a test which you can apply yourself, Clement?

"Now there are more extreme sacrifices which disciples make. Even here there are many pitfalls. When does self-denial spring from genuine love? Have you heard this saying of Jesus? It is similar to the former one.

> " 'When you fast, do not look dismal and disfigure your face as the hypocrites do, that they may win men's notice. I assure you, they have their reward. But when you fast, look natural and joyful, that your fasting may escape men's notice. Then your Father who sees in secret will reward you.'

He who denies himself for the love of Christ is unconscious of his own denial. He finds such joy, such amazing treasure, that he forgets its cost. Does the true lover measure cautiously the cost of his love? Does he pause to congratulate himself on the depth of his love or the extent of popular notice?"

"If this is the way of the Messiah, then I can see how much it differs from the way of Seneca," replied Clement. "In the last analysis, the philosopher is thinking only of himself. He attains peace by forgetting everything else but how to keep his mind from being disturbed. The supreme good is his own happiness. In his mind it is this which justifies even suicide. Above all else he covets an inner assurance of his own courage and tranquillity."

"And that is why our Messiah places love of God and of neighbor above any desire for self-justification," assented Silvanus. "For the disciple, the genuine love of God requires that God's desire rule our hearts. And since God loves men fully, he who serves God must love his neighbor so completely that he forgets his own love. His right hand does not know what his left hand is doing.

"Yes, Clement, this love which the Messiah taught is very different from the self-love of the Stoics. However, there is one thing more that must be pointed out. If this be the way genuine love of God is to be tested—by its cost and by its fruits—what happens to your effort, Clement, to measure your own love? You want to know whether your devotion to the Messiah is as strong as other disciples'. But does God want you to keep weighing your own faithfulness? That leads to hypocrisy or despair. If, when we give alms, we are unaware of our generosity; if, when we fast, we are absorbed in joy, we shall have no inclination to measure the fruit. For, after all, the fruit belongs to Him who planted the seed. Listen to this parable:

"'In the winter the trees shed their leaves and are all alike. And it is not apparent which are dead and which are alive. But in the summer some turn green and blossom while others remain dry and leafless.'

"So this world is winter for the righteous and the sinners alike, and one cannot tell which are alive and which are dead. But the world to come is summer for the righteous. The mercy of the Lord will shine and make plain the fruit of each tree. But this summer will continue to be winter for the sinners. Their trees will remain withered, dry, and fruitless, and they shall be cut down and burned."

CHAPTER 23

The Olive Tree

O N MONDAY evening there was cause for special jubi-
lation in the Church at Della's home, for Marcus
was back. During an absence of several weeks he
had visited Christians in Achaia and Macedonia. Now he
returned with extensive reports. After the worship service
and the common meal, Marcus described conditions
among the Churches in those provinces. The disciples were
relieved to learn that Nero had not pushed his persecution into areas outside of Rome. Though political difficulties were not absent, neither were they acute. In a few
localities magistrates had imprisoned Christians, but this
action had been instigated by opposition within local business circles or by the growing hostility of the synagogue,
rather than by orders from Rome. Not many Jews were
accepting the Messiah, but this decrease was more than
offset by the influx of Gentiles.

Most of the Churches in the east were growing in numbers and enthusiasm. A few, in fact, were growing so rapidly that Churches could hardly assimilate and train so many new converts. These converts, ignorant of the Scriptures and not yet fully trained in the tradition concerning the Messiah, were inclined to headstrong enthusiams. But everywhere men were hungry for the Word. And everywhere the Holy Spirit was setting men free from their slaveries.

Marcus brought a letter from the Church in Corinth to the Churches in Rome, expressing sympathy for their recent losses and confidence in their power to remain loyal. A very substantial gift of money was sent with the letter. After prayers for guidance, the group voted to use a tenth of the fund to buy clothing needed by the orphans, to reserve a tenth as aid for those who might be arrested in the coming weeks, and to send the remainder to the Church at Narcissus' estate, with the suggestion that whatever they did not need might be passed on to the Church in Aquila's home.

Marcus had another unexpected announcement. When Christians in the eastern provinces had heard how many leaders of the Roman Church had been killed, they had decided to send reinforcements, hoping that a more aggressive proclamation of the Gospel would restore the depleted ranks. Titus had come from Dalmatia, and Onesiphorus from Corinth. Both had been in Rome on earlier occasions and knew their way about the city. Both had gained much experience in open-air preaching to audiences of Jews and Gentiles. When Marcus presented these men, the disciples welcomed them with genuine feeling.

It was already late, but before the meeting adjourned the disciples discussed how best to use these reinforcements. At each decision they waited in prayer until the

Holy Spirit had produced a common mind. Everyone was convinced that preaching activity must be renewed in the Forum, the various parks, and the synagogues. To Titus and Marcus fell the assignment of supervising this work. Onesiphorus would spend most of his time with the disciples in the area around Narcissus' estate, trying to gain new recruits for the Church there. Silvanus would complete his work of instruction on the following Sunday. Then he would carry to the Churches in the east letters of thanks for their help, and would stay wherever he was needed for the instruction of new disciples. It was desirable for someone to accompany him, but at the moment there emerged no clear choice for this assignment.

As each decision was reached, the sense of duty and enthusiasm deepened. At the evening's end, the inspiration found an outlet in the singing of a favorite hymn:

"Look! I am laying in Zion a cornerstone, chosen, precious;
    Whoever believes in him will not be put to shame.
The very stone which the masons rejected,
    It has been made the head of the corner.
To unbelievers, a stone of stumbling and a rock of falling
    For, disobeying the word, they stumble
    And thus fulfill their destiny.

"But you are a chosen race, a royal priesthood,
    A holy nation, God's own community,
That you might publish the praises of him
    Who called you out of darkness
    Into his marvelous light.

"Then you knew no community, now you are God's own community;
    Then you received not his blessing, now you have received it."

The first stanza of this hymn served another purpose on the following evening when it became the theme of Marcus' address to the men who were lounging in the Forum and to casual passers-by. For this address, the first open challenge since that evening when the emperor had executed the Christians, Clement accompanied the preacher to the open plaza. It was a cold, gray November evening, but in spite of heavy skies the apostle had little difficulty in attracting and holding a small audience.

Beginning with the Scripture prophecy, the apostle presented Jesus as the cornerstone of God's building. Telling the story of Peter, he reminded the crowd of how the Roman people had murdered Peter. In persecuting the ambassadors of the Messiah, the Romans had in effect joined in crucifying Jesus, the King whom God had sent to save men. How, then, could they escape God's judgment upon the rebellious city unless they changed their minds and hearts?

Marcus' audience were so fascinated by his audacity that they listened spellbound, although the more timid among them shifted slowly to the edge of the group, nervously watching for the police. Oblivious to danger, Marcus concentrated all his thoughts upon his message, tracing the course of events back to the beginning: the appearance of John in the wilderness, the coming of the Spirit on Jesus, the mighty works of healing and forgiveness, the infiltration of God's power into the lives of the disciples, the transforming effect of God's love, the rejection of this love by men for whom it was intended. "The very stone which the masons rejected God has made the cornerstone . . . and this stone has become the foundation of a new house, which God is now building."

Toward the end of the narrative, Clement's imagination was kindled by this picture of the cornerstone. When Marcus closed his appeal for repentance and faith, Clement moved toward the circle's center and asked to say a few words.

"I am a stonemason," he said simply. "When fire destroyed so many houses in this city, a friend and I were brought to Rome to help construct new homes. First we dug deep to lay the foundation. We selected the cornerstone and set it in place. Then, stone by stone, the walls took shape. Each stone had to be smoothed, squared, and fitted. The walls had to be kept solidly based on the foundation, and aligned to the cornerstone. Now the house is almost finished, and the builder must ask: 'How firmly is it built? How long will it last?'

"Now this is a parable of what each of you Roman citizens is doing. Your individual lives are buildings under construction. And together you are building a city for the future. How firmly will your house stand? Of what use will this city be to you?

"In this construction of your life, there is one law which no one can set aside: 'Except God build the house, the men labor in vain who build it.' Unless its foundations be the rock of God's truth, it cannot stand. Unless its cornerstone be the all-supporting purpose of God, the whole structure will be destroyed. Unless the city is built as its true ruler demands, it will be destroyed, and all will perish.

"I told you that I came to Rome to build a house. Thanks be to God, I now know that I have been called to have a part in the building of God's house, a structure that has for its cornerstone the work of Jesus the Messiah. When this house is complete, all earthly structures will be destroyed. I urge you, while there is time, to start building your life on this rock. You must give an answer to God before his temple is finished and before your present home is destroyed."

That night Clement found it impossible to go to sleep. At lightning speed his mind leaped from one recollection to another. He thought again of the three inquirers who had accompanied Marcus and himself back to the house of Della. Next he recalled the wave of astonishment that broke over him when he realized that he had actually confessed Christ openly in the Forum. He had had no intention of speaking, nor had Marcus expected his intrusion. Had he been under a spell? Or was he merely dreaming that he had been in the Forum, the whole scene but a figment of an excited imagination? No, the details of memory were too sharp for that. True, he could not remember clearly just what he had said, but he could visualize exactly the setting and he could hear again the words of Marcus.

Over and over again he compared his present self with the other Clement who had listened so hesitantly to Peter, and who had been baffled by so many questions. How completely those earlier questions had slipped away! How foreign to the new Clement were those worries of that timid country boy venturing for the first time into Rome! He had wondered then what new experiences the year might bring. Now he looked back upon a few short weeks that had ushered him into an entirely strange world and made of him a new person.

It was still true that he knew nothing about tomorrow. The officers might drag him out of bed. Sabinus would probably dismiss him. But he was not now inclined to daydream about countless possibilities. Whatever happened, it could not turn him back again into his old shell. The range of dangers was wider, but his present confidence offered a secure abiding place. Nothing could shake walls which were built on this new foundation. Gradually Clement's thoughts centered about the couplet Marcus had quoted concerning Jesus:

"He who is near me is near the fire;
He who is far from me is far from the kingdom."

On Wednesday evening, Clement crossed the city with Onesiphorus to visit the brothers in Narcissus' household. Again he was included in the upsurge of their gratitude for the gifts from other Churches. Again he was inspired by the strength of the bonds which, by acts of helpfulness, supported the network of Christian love. He was greeted with special warmth by the two men who, on the previous visit, had confessed to him their wavering loyalty. How different was the atmosphere now! Their spirit had shifted from the defensive to the aggressive. Once more the witness to the Messiah was joyful and unafraid. A wedge had been driven into a neighboring estate by the conversion of two slaves and a foreman. To be sure, Narcissus had not modified his tactics. Some of the brothers bore the scars of recent floggings, and one had been disowned and banned from the premises. The gifts of money had come just in time to prevent real hardship.

The park on the Flaminian Way no longer had the atmosphere of a hide-out of depressed fugitives. Rather, the air seemed charged with energy and expectancy. The words of Onesiphorus brought immediate response. Eagerly the brothers accepted his offer of help. And without delay they began to map their strategy, connecting the network by which invitations could be carried to outsiders. Onesiphorus would speak in the park every evening, and the others would seek personal conversations with nonbelievers who attended. Search would be made immediately for a place with rooms large enough for indoor meetings. This would enable the group to be less dependent upon the owner's whim and the winter weather.

It was all that Clement could do to keep pace in his thoughts with the rapid extension of his activities. He had become completely absorbed in the life of the new community, filled with joy over his inner certainties. The addresses of the apostles, the repeated hours with Silvanus, the regular attendance at worship and the common meal, the enlarging horizons of connections with other Churches, the deepening sense of togetherness with the disciples—all these were richly satisfying.

Yet with each lull in activity Clement became conscious of things still undone. He was responsible for making decisions which could no longer be postponed. The longer he delayed, the more sensitive his conscience became. He must send an answer to his father. And he must arrive at a more permanent agreement with Sabinus. Before writing to his father he must learn more of Sabinus' plans.

The impromptu speech in the Forum made it impossible to delay any longer the talk with Sabinus. The parable of the building stones made Clement acutely conscious that his heart was no longer in his work as a mason. He had been careful to spend the same number of hours on the job and had tried to maintain the same quality of workmanship. But the prospect of starting another house for Sabinus had lost its attraction. Could he force himself to continue a vocation toward which he had grown cold? And if he gave it up, how would he support himself?

His conscience also smarted from the realization that his speech in the Forum might endanger Sabinus. Clement had promised not to involve his employer in his illegal activities. He had kept the letter of that promise, but he realized that everything he was doing made Sabinus' position more vulnerable. Perhaps the police had heard Clement's inflammatory remarks at the synagogue or in the Forum. Sooner or later they would spot him and would trace his connections. Honesty demanded that he give his employer fair warning.

Clement had also promised not to disturb the other workers in Sabinus' staff. But what if they saw and heard him in one of the Christian gatherings? He could not then avoid breaking his promise. The original agreement had been for a trial period of two weeks. That time had now elapsed, and a more permanent settlement must be made.

Clement found his master quite ready to discuss the situation. No, he had not changed his estimate of the Church, nor had his fears of the police diminished. He was alarmed when Clement told him that he had spoken in the Forum as a Christian. And his alarm turned to anger when Clement told him that he could no longer keep his pledge not to disturb the other workers on the building. Before Clement had finished, Sabinus blurted out: "You have made your own decision. Unless you keep your promise, I cannot keep mine. This week you and Julian will finish the more difficult stonelaying on this building. I had planned to move you to another project, but you have made that impossible now. After this job is finished, two choices are open to you. One is to go back home to my country place, where you can't do much damage. The other is to leave my employ and find another job for yourself. If you do that, of course, you will have to take very low wages, for you will be competing with slaves."

Although the tone of the interview was far from heartening, Clement found that when it was over the burden on his shoulders was much lighter. For one thing, his conscience was clear. For another, he found himself happy that his building days in Rome were nearly over. Spending his energies in tasks from which his interests had drained had been a more severe strain than he had realized.

It was also a relief to have the complex situation clarified. There remained for him only the choice Sabinus had suggested: to return home or to remain in Rome and search for independent employment. Sabinus had permitted him to delay his decision until the first of the following week. It would be far from easy, but at least the alternatives were clear and sharp. He knew well what was ahead of him if he returned to the country. If he stayed in Rome, the prospect was different. He was aware that Sabinus' warning about his financial insecurity in Rome was sound. Though always a freedman, Clement had never realized what it would mean to be a free man. Since he was not a citizen, many doors which Sabinus had opened for him would now be closed. He was free now to starve or to barter his labor from day to day in a slave market. He was free to go where he pleased, but also free from the protection and security of an assured living on a large estate. And he could not turn to the Church for support.

Even with this dubious prospect, Clement left work that evening in buoyant spirits. He was grateful that his employer had been so clearheaded and definite. He was grateful that his own store of Christian courage was proving more than adequate to dispel anxiety.

The only thing that rankled in his mind was the way in which Julian had reacted. When Clement had told him that this would be their last week together, and that then he would either return home or break loose entirely, Julian had spurted out in angry sarcasm: "Perhaps that will drive some reason into your stubborn head."

Clement declined to answer this attack.

"You haven't been the same person since you began

keeping company with Christians. Sabinus is quite right. In his shoes, I would have done the same, only sooner." Finding no resistance, Julian's attack had gradually subsided. "It will be a good thing for you to go back home. You'll soon forget all your involvements here. You weren't ready for Rome in the first place."

How quickly a lifelong friendship can evaporate, Clement thought sadly.

On Saturday morning Marcus invited Clement to accompany him to the Synagogue of the Olive Tree, and Clement accepted gladly. Perhaps Bar-Joseph would be there; if so, there might be another opportunity for reconciliation. Should Bar-Joseph be more friendly, Clement might ask his advice on the issue at hand. Too, Clement had a deep sense of belonging to this synagogue. It represented in some degree his home and his people, and while there he might arrive at an answer to send his father. On the way to the Janiculan hill, he talked over his problem with Marcus.

Bar-Joseph was present at the synagogue, but Clement's opportunity was lost, because Marcus' address served to destroy all chance of reconciliation. The apostle, to be sure, began in his most gracious manner. He mentioned the hostility of the synagogue, and then asked why Christian disciples should wish to come back time and again to preach. It was their love for their people, he explained, and their unwillingness to see God's elect forfeit their heritage. They had cherished the covenants, and as sons of God had maintained the service of God through fire and flood. The promises had been made to their fathers, and fulfilled in a Messiah who had come to them and given his life for them. No people on earth had been so marvelously blessed as they. Why, then, had Israel failed to accept and follow this Saviour?

All were sons of Abraham's flesh, Marcus pointed out, but not all were sons of Abraham's faith. Abraham, Isaac, Jacob—each had had many children, but in each generation there had been those who had been lost by unbelief and others who had been saved by their faith.

Pointing to the name of this synagogue, Marcus compared the congregation to an olive tree planted by God. In these last days, God visited this tree, in the hope of finding faith. Having planted it, the right to harvest its fruit is his. How much did he find? Sons of Abraham's flesh and sons of Abraham's faith, yes; but how many productive branches? Only a handful. Most branches he found withered, requiring to be cut out. The fruitful branches must be pruned and trained to produce more heavily. New branches from a wild olive tree must be grafted in, so that the tough roots might fulfill their tasks.

Noting a ripple of resentment, the speaker then made a gesture of understanding: "We who are disciples of the Messiah know full well the reasons for your displeasure. We too were offended at first by the good news. When apostles proclaimed that Jesus had been exalted to heaven, we too said, 'Nonsense!' When they proclaimed that this crucified Man had been raised from the dead, we too said, 'Who has come back from the dead whose word can be trusted?' But we found that God's word is as near as the believing heart. We found that the venture of faith alone can bring assurance that this message is in fact true—that Jesus both was killed and has been raised. What is needed is not more convincing evidence of this message, but a heart that repents and confesses in simple trust that Jesus is Lord. After that first faltering step, God floods the heart with confidence. He is rich in mercy to all who call upon him. Trust him and he will lead you into his own blessed Kingdom. Make this synagogue God's 'olive tree' in truth.

Let not the branches wither in unbelief, but blossom in faith."

It was Bar-Joseph who brought Marcus' address to a close. His words were blazing with heat. "So! You are the fruitful branches, and we are withered and sterile. You are blessed; the rest of us are damned. If other traitors are present, let them join you. You have cut yourselves away from us forever. Do not suppose that you can graft yourselves back as a branch of our tree whenever your new infatuation vanishes."

The crowd supposed that the elder was attacking Marcus. Clement realized, however, that the words were really meant for him. It was Bar-Joseph's way of saying: "Son, this is your last chance. If you go on being a Christian, don't ever return to this synagogue."

It was a sober Clement who appeared for his last day's work on the Esquiline.

CHAPTER 24

Waiting for the Spirit

"Blessed be the God and Father of our Lord, Jesus Christ,
  Who has blessed us with heavenly treasure and spiritual
    grace.
  He chose us to be his sons through Jesus Christ;
  He made known to us the mystery of his purposes;
  He opened the eyes of our hearts to believe in his power;
  He forgave us our sins and gave us a share in his right-
    eousness;
  He healed our diseases and declared peace to our war-
    ring passions;
  He canceled the power of death and made us heirs of
    life.
  O the depth of the riches and wisdom and grace of God!
  For from him and through him and to him are all things.
  Blessed be his name forever."

THE whole class was aware that this was the final session with Silvanus. They knew too that after this hour of instruction they would be expected to take full responsibilities as members of the Church. None of them felt prepared to cope with all the situations they must face as servants of Christ in a hostile world. The teacher had prepared carefully for making the hour memorable.

The first part of the time was spent in recalling the signposts along the road they had covered. Silvanus would give them a clue by reciting the first few words of a memorized teaching; then the class would complete it.

> " 'Wide is the gate, easy to find the road . . .
> " 'Two men went up to the temple to pray . . .
> " 'A man had two sons . . .
> " 'As it happened in the days of Noah . . .
> " 'You have put off the old self . . .
> " 'Be merciful, that you may obtain mercy . . .
> " 'It is as a man traveling in another country . . .
> " 'No man who puts his hand to the plow . . .
> " 'Ask, and it will be given . . .
> " 'No man can serve two masters . . .' "

After satisfying himself that these pivots were driven firmly into the minds of the students, Silvanus asked them which pivot would best serve as the summary of all the rest. No two answers agreed; each had found a different saying to be the central point around which the others revolved in their minds. To Gaius, the command which seemed to contain all the rest was the injunction, "Put on the Lord Jesus Christ." Silvanus suggested a longer version of this saying which made its major implications clear:

> " 'Do not be conformed to this world
> But be transformed by the renewal of your mind,
> That you may prove what is the will of God,
> What is good and praiseworthy and perfect.' "

Quintus approved this, but protested that it was too general to give enough specific guidance in limited situations. "Is there a summary," he asked, "that would be more detailed?"

Silvanus answered after some thought: "If you will consider this rule as the hub of a wheel, you can add the spokes which connect the hub to the rim. At each moment the hub is connected with the ground through a different spoke, and many spokes are necessary to complete a wheel. Once the axis of a Christian's life has been fixed, then his new mind may be trusted to make the connection with each situation. In dealing with any person, the disciple is conscious at each moment that he must serve the Lord. Thus the mind of the Messiah covers each successive segment of the disciple's path." To show what he meant by spokes, Silvanus gave these commands:

> " 'Rejoice in hope
> Be patient in suffering
> Be constant in prayer
> Rejoice with those who rejoice
> Weep with those who weep
> Practice hospitality
> Never be conceited
> Associate with the humble
> Never flag in zeal
> Be aglow with the Spirit
> Bless those who persecute you
> Do not be overcome by evil
> Overcome evil with good
> Love your neighbor as yourself.' "

"The hub, with those spokes, may be called the Christian's wheel. This is a summary of all that we have studied. But I hope it is clear that it is not enough for the disciple to memorize these teachings. By themselves they do not solve our problems for us. In fact, they often produce more difficulties than they remove. The way in which our

Master teaches us is to make us face a hard situation. As we struggle to come to a decision, we learn the vivid truth of his commands. No matter how alone you may feel, remember that Jesus is there in that very solitude, trying to teach you what it means to follow him.

"Right now, for example, each of you is probably wrestling with a dilemma that seems too big for you to conquer. That is the place where the Master is giving you instruction."

"You can surely read our minds," laughed Clement. "The more I study my problem, the harder it gets. Should I return home or stay in Rome?"

Sara's problem was a similar one. Her parents were becoming so alarmed over her activities in the Church that she was virtually banned from the synagogue and might soon be expelled from her home. Cornelia, as a slave, was most bothered by her responsibility toward her owner. How often must she disobey him because of her new allegiance? Gaius also mentioned the same difficulty—increasing friction with his owner.

Silvanus launched first into the duties of a Christian slave. "In every action," he began, "we must start with Christ and not with the world, following the will of our heavenly Lord rather than the will of our earthly master. Now the Messiah has treated all men in love, thinking not of their rank among men but of their rank before God. Therefore, to one whose mind has been transformed according to his pattern, there can be no distinction between Greek and Jew, circumcised and uncircumcised, slave and free man; Christ is all and in all."

"Does this mean, then, that I am really no longer a slave at all?" asked Cornelia.

"Yes. Before God all of us are equal. Within our fellowship there can be no discrimination. Christ has done away with all such barriers."

"Here in Della's house I find no difficulty," replied Cornelia. "You have all treated me as an equal. And I can't tell you what that means to one who has been a slave all her life. But the problem is whether or not to obey my owner, who is not a Christian. Sometimes he orders me to do things which the Messiah would not tolerate. Should I refuse? Ought I to run away?"

"Not necessarily. Remember that God loves your owner as much as he loves you. In your attitude toward him you must try to please neither him nor yourself, but the Lord. This is the rule that the Apostle Paul taught us:

> " 'Slaves, obey your earthly masters.
> Not with eyeservice, as pleasing men,
> But in singleness of heart, as fearing the Lord.
> Whatever your task, work heartily,
> As serving the Lord and not men,
> Knowing that you shall receive a reward
> From the Lord whom you serve.' "

Cornelia was inclined to argue the point vigorously. "But doesn't this make me more of a slave than ever? Am I to have no independence at all?"

"The rule works both ways. If you disobey your owner just because you want to make things easier for yourself, you are making the Messiah a slave of your own self-interest. You have forgotten that he is Lord. But, on the other hand, if you obey your owner just in order to receive his praise, then too you have become double-minded. As long as the Messiah is your only master, as long as you serve him in every act, then your heart is freed from fear of your owner and from your own selfishness."

"If this is true, then how can a Christian slave ever expect to escape his slavery?" It was not hard to see that Cornelia had made up her mind to leave her owner.

"Can you serve Christ even though you remain bound to your owner?"

"I have been trying to."

"Would you escape from all difficulties if these chains were broken? Can a Christian expect to escape from all tyrannies, to become independent of all institutions and all obligations to the existing society?"

"I suppose not," replied Cornelia. "Perhaps Quintus and Sara have no easier life than mine."

"One more question." Silvanus did not usually bear down so heavily on one point. But this was a principle which must be driven home. "Did Jesus try to free himself from all the obligations which connected him to the institutions of the age? Did he teach that men must achieve political freedom or financial independence in order to enter the Kingdom?"

"I'm afraid you have me there," admitted Cornelia. "The only answer, of course, is, 'No.' If the Messiah accepted all these human restrictions, you mean that his disciples can hardly claim to be exempted from them?"

"That's just what I mean. This is the principle that disciples follow:

" 'Everyone should remain in the state in which he was called. Were you a slave when called? The Lord has assigned you this life, so accept it without anxiety . . . .

" 'He who was called in the Lord as a slave
Is a freedman of the Lord.
He who was called in the Lord as a free man
Is a slave of the Lord.' "

Silvanus could see that Cornelia did not relish this seemingly harsh treatment of her case. And he appreciated how galling slavery like hers could become. Yet he could not, with a clear conscience, encourage her dreams of an easy escape. "It may be, of course, that someday your owner will offer you freedom. In that case, you should take advantage of it. Or if it becomes clear to you and to all of us that our Master has a special work for you to do that requires your freedom, our Church may be able to collect enough money to purchase it. But a change in your status depends upon the Lord's will and not upon your own desires."

"Does this same principle apply to my problem?" inquired Clement. "The Law commands a son to obey his father. Must I treat him as Cornelia treats her owner, and obey the command to return home?"

"Can you go home without yielding your faith in Jesus?"

"That would be difficult, but I think it would be possible."

"Perhaps God has a special duty for you to do at home."

"I have been considering that. But I have also been thinking of the word from Jesus which you taught us: 'No man who loves his parents more than me is worthy of me.' What does that mean in my case?"

"Yes, there are many teachings like that. This one, for example:

"'Do you suppose that I have come to bring peace on
      earth?
   No, I tell you that I have come to bring division.
   From now on five members of one house will be divided,
                  Three against two,
                  Two against three;
                  Father against son,
                  Son against father;
                  Mother against daughter,
                  Daughter against mother.'"

"But, teacher, that seems to be a flat contradiction." Cornelia returned to the argument, sensing that her case was involved in Clement's. "How can the Messiah ask us to do both of these things: to remain in the state in which he called us, and to be divided, father against son and slave against owner?"

"It sounds impossible, doesn't it? But it really is not. When our families forbid us to follow the Messiah, we have but one course. On the other hand, God has placed us in our families for a purpose of his own, and has commanded us to obey our parents. In whatever we do we must act because of our love for him. If we obey, we obey in the Lord. If we disobey, we disobey in the Lord.

"There comes to my memory a story about our Lord. Once when he was going along a road, he saw a man plowing a field on the Sabbath day. Jesus said to him: 'Man, if you know what you are doing, you are blessed. If you don't know, you are accursed, and a transgressor of the Law.' If you disobey your parents through loyalty to Christ, you are blessed; but if you disobey because you want an easier life for yourself, then you are accursed."

Clement was dissatisfied. "But that doesn't help me at all. I must decide before tomorrow. One part of me wants to return home; the other part wants to stay here. And I have no way of knowing what my real motives are. The Messiah has given me no sign of his will."

"This is one reason why disciples must spend so much time in prayer. It is not easy to know exactly what the Lord intends. Often he means to teach us patience by concealing his will. But when he wants us to know his will, if we are fully humble, he sends the Holy Spirit to uncover our secret motives and to point out the path of love. Sometimes the hardest duty is simply to wait."

Such a solution satisfied neither Clement nor Cornelia. Both of them were very eager to arrive at a more certain decision, and Silvanus' position appeared to evade their difficulty rather than to solve it. But neither of them knew how to refute their teacher. Silvanus sensed their rebellion, but made no effort to meet it. The other students were also aware of the rift, and were relieved when Joseph turned the discussion into a new channel.

It was the problem of marriage that he raised. Some disciples were married to unbelievers, and there was friction between husband and wife. Some were single, and might wish to marry; some were married and might wish to gain a divorce. Silvanus reported first on the general practice of the Churches.

> " 'Wives, be subject to your husbands, as is fitting in the Lord.
> Husbands, love your wives, and do not be harsh to them.

> " 'Are you bound to a wife? Do not seek to be free.
> Are you free from a wife? Do not seek to be married.
> But if you marry, you do not sin,
> And if a woman marries she does not sin.
> But it is well for a person to remain as he is.

> " 'If a brother has a wife who is an unbeliever,
> And she consents to live with him,
> He should not divorce her.
> If a sister has a husband who is an unbeliever,
> And he consents to live with her,
> She should not divorce him.
> For God has a purpose in this union.
> But if the unbelieving partner desires to separate,
> Let it be done; in such a case the disciple is not bound;
> For God has called us to peace.' "

"That rule seems to cover everything," commented Joseph in admiration. "Wouldn't it be well for us to memorize it?" The class agreed, and repeated it until the words were fixed. Then Joseph continued:

"I have not said much about my family life because in the past it has created few difficulties for me. I am married to an unbeliever. But Martha is faithful to the Law of

Moses and does not want me to divorce her. Lately, however, she has been hearing at the synagogue a great deal of gossip and slander about us disciples. She has begun to believe it, and she wants me to give up my activities here. I refuse, of course. But the more I refuse, the less pleasant things become at home."

"Marriage may become difficult," Silvanus replied, "but we can still treat the marriage relation as sacred. As a husband, Joseph, God has bound you to your wife. The two of you are one. You are therefore called to love your wife in the same ways that you love yourself. You are called to love her as the Messiah loves her. It should be no more possible for you to despise her than to despise your own flesh, or than the Messiah despises our flesh. Our bodies are his temple. They become the place where we worship him and the instruments by which we serve him.

> " 'None of us lives to himself.
> None of us dies to himself.
> If we live, we live to the Lord;
> If we die, we die to the Lord.
> Whether we live or whether we die,
> We are the Lord's.
> For to this end Christ died and lived again,
> That he might be the Lord of the dead and of the
>   living.' "

Now it was Quintus' turn to introduce a different range of problems: "My difficulties are those of a soldier in uniform. I know that the time will come when my commanding officer will require me to do something prohibited by the Messiah. Then I shall be forced to defy one master or the other."

"Yes, you will be caught in the conflict between God and the world. Yet God has a purpose in having called you when you are a soldier. It may be that he calls you to serve the Lord Jesus by obeying your superiors. It may be that he will call you to serve the Lord Jesus by refusing to obey them. Like every other disciple, you must seek the mind of Christ so that his love may flow through your life into the lives of others. His Spirit will enable you to know what love for him requires of you. Perhaps I can summarize all these obligations for you.

> " 'In love fulfill all obligations;
> Pay to each man what is due:
> Taxes to whom taxes are due,
> Revenue to whom revenue is due,
> Respect to whom respect is due,
> Honor to whom honor is due.' "

Now that so many different duties had been examined, Clement was eager to lead the conversation back toward his own immediate problem. As yet Silvanus had not made the decision much easier for him. Clement still would have to choose for himself whether he should return home or defy his father's summons and stay in Rome. In one way that decision was now easier in that he realized the importance of following the guidance of the Spirit. In another way, it was more difficult simply because there was no rule of thumb which could settle the matter for him. And Silvanus was unwilling to advise him.

What use has the Messiah for me? he mused. *I can see what he may assign me to do at home. He may want me to talk with my parents about the Christian faith and try to gather new disciples there. But if he wants me to stay in Rome at the expense of defying my family, what would be his purpose? Is there some special task for me here?*

Finally he phrased the question so that it would apply to all the students. "Teacher, we have been preparing for future work as disciples. To each of us will be given special assignments within the Church. How may we know what this work is to be?"

"It is not for us to pick the most desirable post for ourselves." Silvanus wished to undercut traits of ambition that had already shown themselves among his students. "Nor is it fitting for us to hurry into decisions of this sort. Haste in selecting our separate jobs is usually the sign of ambition and jealousy. We must each wait for the Spirit to open the doors. In some cases the Spirit gives to your inner ear a direct call to preach or to teach. In some cases the Spirit speaks through the voice of the Church, as we pray together for guidance. Since there is only one Spirit, this does not lead to confusion or grumbling. Dissension among us indicates that we are not placing first the love of God.

"The Apostle Paul gave us a true picture of how the Spirit works within us all to lead us toward a single goal:

" 'Together we are the body of Christ;
Individually we are members of it.
Just as the body has many members and yet is one.
So also the body of Christ has many members and yet is one.
For by one Spirit we were all baptized into one body,
And all were made to drink of one Spirit.
Now there are varieties of gifts, but the same Spirit;

There are varieties of service, but the same Lord;
There are varieties of working, but the same God
Who inspires them all in every one.

" 'To each is given the manifestation of the Spirit
For the common good.
To one is given through the Spirit the utterance of wisdom;
To another faith by the same Spirit;
To another gifts of healing by the one Spirit;
To another the working of miracles;
To another prophecy;
To another the ability to distinguish between spirits;
To another various kinds of tongues;
To another the interpretation of tongues.

" 'All these are inspired by the same Spirit,
    Who apportions to each one individually as he wills.'

"As you wait for the Spirit to indicate your own particu-
lar vocation, do not fail to remember that already the
Spirit has assigned you definite tasks. The Spirit commands
us all to trust in God; it commands us ever to hope for his
Kingdom; it commands us to love, and love itself gives
us our tasks, enough to keep us busy every day. When one
suffers, all of us suffer. When one rejoices, all of us rejoice.
When one is in need, all of us are involved in discovering
strength to meet that need. When one sins, the rest of us
must forgive him, trying to draw him back into an un-
broken fellowship. Nothing that we have is our own, nor
do we call it our own, because everything has been given
us by our common Lord. Whatever our resources, they
are at his disposal. Because he is creating the Church as
his temple, every manifestation of his Spirit is directed
toward the construction of the temple where love reigns.

"This, then, is the picture that I leave with you—a picture of the Church as a building under construction. The
foundation has been laid. Each of us is a stone in it. Each
choice of ours retards or advances the construction.

"Listen now to a parable from our Lord:

" 'He who hears my words and obeys them
    Will be like a wise man who built his house upon rock.
    The rains fell; floods came; tempests beat upon it;
    But the house did not fall.
    It had been founded on rock.

" 'He who hears my words and disobeys them
    Will be like a foolish man who built his house on sand.
    The rains fell; floods came; tempests beat upon it;
    And the house fell.
    It had been founded on sand.' "

CHAPTER 25

Crossroads

SOMETIMES the hardest duty is simply to wait."

Thus Silvanus had taught, warning Clement against impatience in making his decision. But that teaching was not sufficient to *make* him patient. He must have the answer by tomorrow, so he spent the day trying to force his mind into a clear-cut choice. The alternatives were definite enough. He could return home, continue his work for Sabinus on the country estate, and be alert for opportunities to tell his associates about Jesus. Perhaps God wanted him to be the messenger who would start a new Church there. But this picture exerted no special pull, no inner attraction that would mark it as God's will for him. What if he stayed in Rome? Rejecting his family obligations, he could find employment as a mason. He could continue to live at Della's house and to work with the disciples. He was quite ready to do this, but he felt no conviction or enthusiasm about it.

All day long, as he balanced these possibilities, his restlessness increased. This was the first day of his leisure from work on the Esquiline, and he had nothing to do but debate with himself. But the longer he debated, the farther he was from making up his mind. He could not sit still, but aimlessly roamed the streets. Passing several employment exchanges, he was inclined to investigate the openings for masons, but he knew he was not ready to accept a position should he find one.

The splinter of resentment pierced deeper into his mind. Why had Silvanus so stubbornly refused to give advice, treating his dilemma so casually? Why hadn't the other disciples been more helpful? Were they all too absorbed in their own problems to be aware of his? Silvanus had insisted that a disciple must wait for the Spirit to open the doors. But here was a door that wouldn't wait. Here was a stretch of road uncharted by the teachings of Jesus. At great risk he had joined the Church; now the Church failed to give him instruction. He had resolved to obey God's command; now God was silent. Did God always leave his servants in the dark about specific choices like this one? Deeper and deeper worked the splinter.

Evening came, but Clement was in no mood for worship, no mood for joining the other disciples. Since they had failed to help in this emergency, there was no point in going back until he knew what he was going to do. He recalled, however, that Silvanus was leaving tomorrow. This might be the last opportunity to see him. He owed him too much to be churlish about his failure to provide guidance in this one situation. So he returned.

His participation in prayers and benedictions was listless; his thoughts were too tangled to permit a hearty response. Even the words of the leader, Rufus, failed to penetrate the inner turmoil. He kept telling himself to pay attention and chiding himself for not doing so. He blamed himself for coming at all, and blamed the others for their lack of concern. He felt suddenly estranged from the fellowship, even more than when he had first attended as an inquirer.

In desperation he was considering leaving the meeting when some words of the speaker caught his attention:

"Ask, and you will receive,
    Seek, and you will find;
    Knock, and the door will be opened."

But that just isn't true, Clement protested to himself. *I have committed myself to God's will. Yet when I ask for guidance, no answer comes. When I knock, the door remains shut. All I need is a single signpost at this crossroads. And that I must have. But God is silent. Doesn't it matter to him? Has he deceived me?*

Suddenly he felt himself completely isolated in space— cut off from family, spurned by former friends, estranged from the other disciples, abandoned by God. The agony of this isolation blotted from his mind the restless groping for a decision about tomorrow. Now he was alone, dreadfully alone, on a wind-swept desert, the barren sands stretching endlessly in every direction. His whole life took the shape of a single question: "Where, now, is your God?" And to this question no word came from the emptiness. *Is this, then, the final answer—that there can be no answer? Do we seek God only to find him gone when we need him most?*

A dim echo came to his ears, a line of Scripture reverberating through the silences:

"If with all your heart you truly seek me,
You will ever surely find me,
Thus says the Lord."

It's not so, was Clement's first reaction. Then he detected a peculiar accent on the word "all." *Am I seeking God with all my heart?* he wondered.

But, of course, I am, Clement instinctively defended himself. *Surely my willingness to sacrifice proves that I am seeking God with all my heart.*

How do you know that? The questioner was not so easily satisfied.

Haven't I risked my life in becoming a Christian? Haven't I lost my job because of it? I am even willing to break with my home for the sake of my faith.

Aren't you forgetting something?

What greater tests are there?

Haven't you forgotten what you heard this morning? Is impatience a sign of trust? Are nervous worries a mark of obedience? Is self-concern among the works of love?

Clement felt himself maneuvered into a trap, and he tried to escape. *But a decision is before me, and I must know. I can't postpone it, like Silvanus and the others.*

The questions ceased, and Clement was back on the barren desert, alone. He had defended himself successfully, but he was alone. Was this loneliness a sign of success? Then, at once, something else happened. An image flickered across the screen of his mind; it returned and stayed.

It was the image of a man. He was naked and nailed to a cross. He was dead. No, he was alive and was speaking. What did he say? Something about trust and joy—yes, and victory.

The picture vanished and the words faded out. But the

echoes remained. Was this the same voice that had been questioning him earlier? Clement could not tell. He knew only that the isolation had been broken. The desert was no longer empty. In desperation and desolation Clement had sought God and had failed. But Jesus had been seeking Clement, and had found him.

Is this, then, the way in which God breaks the silence? Does he drive man into the desert in order that the Messiah may find him there? I asked . . . no answer . . . then Jesus spoke. Is this Man on the cross all I need to know of God? Is he all I need to look for?

There tumbled into his mind phrase after phrase of the teachings of Jesus, which Silvanus had so carefully taught. There came also the stories of Jesus' deeds, as told by Peter, Marcus, and Rufus. There came memories of Jesus' suffering, and memories of the common meals with the disciples. Snatches from the hymns and benedictions floated through the air. *Jesus was an actual man, through whom God has offered his help to me. God has sent him to me to break through my solitude.*

Impetuously Clement's thoughts moved forward, leaping from one discovery to another. In Jesus, God is not only answering questions. He is showing too what questions men ought to ask; how a son should knock at the door of life's mysteries.

For Jesus was a son who took the long, lonely road, and found a path for others to follow. His humility, his patience, his self-forgetfulness, his trust, his courage—these are the doors that open the way. He didn't know what the future might hold, but he wasn't concerned about his own fate. He didn't demand that God make the road easier. He didn't give way to doubts of God's power. He didn't assault the doors which he thought God *should* open, but confidently waited for the guiding Spirit to open them.

Another discovery: Why had not the despair which tormented Clement trapped Jesus? Because his obedience to God had made him forget his own worries in concern for others. Jesus had not asked, "What does God owe me in exchange for my sacrifice?" but, "How can I free men—lepers, slaves, harlots, sinners—from their bondage?" The only way to enter the circle of Jesus' love was to include in that circle all whom Jesus loved. Bar-Joseph belonged there, and his father, and Sabinus, and Julian.

These discoveries so absorbed Clement that he was hardly aware that his own problem no longer troubled him. He was surprised too to realize that all resentments had evaporated; that both his isolation from God and his estrangement from the disciples had vanished. He was actually standing in the new world which Jesus had created.

Still in a daze from the impacts of these rapid discoveries, Clement was hardly aware that the public meeting had now closed and that the disciples were moving into the adjoining room for their common meal. On earlier occasions parts of this observance had inspired him, but never had the deep meanings of the rite fully penetrated the inner recesses of his heart. Now he realized, as if for the first time, that the believers were actually eating in fellowship with this crucified Jesus who had made a path between heaven and earth. Other disciples too were experiencing the revolution through which he had just come.

As the cup was held up, Marcus gave thanks.

"We give thanks to thee, our Father, for the holy vine of David thy child, which thou didst make known to us through Jesus thy Child. To thee be glory forever."

Clement thought: *It is not Marcus who hands this to us, but Jesus himself. He it is who serves our table, who provides this blood as a covenant with him. Jonas once said*

that Jesus promised to drink with us at his table in the
Kingdom of God. Is this then that meal of fellowship in
the Kingdom itself?

Marcus lifted up the plate of bread and gave thanks.

"We give thee thanks, our Father, for the life and knowledge which thou didst make known to us through Jesus
thy Child. To thee be glory forever."

They ate in silence, knowing that if the love of Jesus
fully captured their wills, their lives would become a part
of his life, given for men. The silence was full of activity,
full of mutual gratitude. The risen Lord was even now
strengthening the invisible cords that knit them together.
Clement recalled the teaching memorized that morning:
"Together we are the body of Christ." Like Clement, the
others had not fully appreciated its profound implications, but this Sacrament helped to establish them. The
group joined heartily in the closing prayer:

"As this broken bread was scattered upon the mountains,
but was brought together and became one, so let thy
Church be gathered together from the ends of the earth
into thy Kingdom. For thine is the glory and the power,
through Jesus Christ, forever. Amen."

The disciples lingered after the meal. There was important business to be settled. First, the approval of letters
which Marcus and Titus had written to the Churches
which had sent such generous aid. A letter of introduction
for Silvanus was among them. There was also a letter giving a report on the work which Titus and Onesiphorus had
begun.

Then Marcus presented the problem of choosing a
brother to accompany Silvanus. No one had been found to
meet all the requirements. Because the work would con-
sist of training new converts, someone was needed who

was well grounded in the Scriptures and who knew well the teachings of Jesus. It would be a rigorous life, filled with travel and uncertainty. The man would have to support himself by a trade of his own. In all probability, he would become embroiled in controversies with the synagogue and with the police.

There was a period of silent praying for the Spirit's guidance in this selection. As the minutes went by Clement was thinking over the possibilities (*Marcus is needed here, Sara and Cornelia are not free, Quintus . . .*). Then suddenly he heard one of the deacons saying: "Some time ago Clement and I made a trip to the brothers at Narcissus' estate. We took them baskets of food and tried to encourage them. When my companion was speaking, I noticed the contagious power of his words for those who were discouraged. I felt then that God was preparing Clement for a special duty of some sort, and I feel now that he is the one called to go with Silvanus."

Then Sara, who had never before participated in community decisions, recalled that on the steps of the Synagogue of the Olive Tree after a Sabbath service not long ago, Clement had felt impelled to address the worshipers, and that on this occasion too his words had power to move both his own people and Gentiles.

Della, who like Sara seldom expressed herself in meeting, felt moved too to say that her mind had turned toward Clement. She reminded them of his courage, while he was still only an inquirer, in warning them of Nero's plans. In a low voice she told of the evening when Jonas and the others had been killed. "It was on that evening," she concluded, "that Jesus drew Clement into our fellowship. Ever since, I have felt that God intended him to carry on my husband's work. Now I believe that the hour has arrived for him to begin."

Silvanus turned to his student. "Have you anything you feel should be said?"

Clement did not answer at once. The suggestion had struck him with something approaching physical shock, and he could not quickly gather his words together.

"Until these three spoke, the thought had never occurred to me. I am not worthy for this mission. Nor am I prepared. In fact, today and this evening I have been guilty of rebellion against God and have felt estranged from all of you. But just before we ate our meal together, Jesus on his cross came before my mind, and brought back the joy of belonging to him. If it is his will, I am ready to go. In my heart, I know that this is the answer I have been seeking."

The farewell prayers and benedictions were in word and spirit something to remember always. Clement could not linger, for if he were to be ready for tomorrow's departure, there were preparations to be made before retiring. First he packed his knapsack and planned what he would say to Julian and Sabinus in the morning. Then he settled down by the lamp to write the letter to his parents. He did not finish until hours after Silvanus had gone to sleep. Finally he crawled wearily onto his pallet, saying to himself, "I am ready now, at last, for anything the future may bring."

*   *   *

CLEMENT TO HIS FATHER MATTATHIAS, GREETING:

I am grateful for the concern which prompted your last letter to me. Always you have done what you thought best for me, and you must know that I would not easily disregard your advice. I shall always respect my obligations to you and to Bar-Joseph, who has been faithful to your wishes.

In spite of your request and Bar-Joseph's discouragement, I cannot consider surrendering my allegiance to Jesus, into whose service God has called me.

You asked me to come home. I have delayed an answer until I knew God's will. At Sabinus' request I stopped work on his house yesterday. This left me free to return home, but I was still uncertain whether that was the right decision.

Tonight my place became clear to me and to those in the Christian fellowship. The brothers have decided to send two of us, my teacher Silvanus and myself, to visit other Churches in Achaia, Macedonia, and possibly even Judea. We leave tomorrow. It is an important mission, one which I did not expect and which I cannot refuse without disloyalty.

I find myself completely and joyously absorbed in the prospect of my new faith, and with greater peace of spirit than I have ever known.

As soon as we return from the east, I shall come to see you, probably in the early spring. And it may be that then I will settle down once more in the work on the plantation. But until then I must carry out this assignment that God has given me. I have no fears, but only the hope that I may be faithful—as faithful as you have been through the years.

Let us trust that God knows what is best for us all. May he bless you always with his grace and peace.

BIBLICAL AND OTHER SOURCES

PAGES   CHAPTER 1
15.......Num. 29:1–6
18.......Gen., chs. 21; 22
19.......Gen. 22:17, 18
20.......I Sam., ch. 2

CHAPTER 3
36.......Yotzer: cf. Oesterley,
          *Jewish Background of
          the Christian Liturgy,*
          p. 48
37.......'Ahabah: *ibid.*
38.......Deut. 6:4–7
39. .....Deut. 11:16; Num.
          15:39, 40
40.......Deut. 29:10–21
41.......Deut. 30:1–10
43.......Jer. 30:12–15
43.......Jer. 30:18–22

CHAPTER 4
48.......Luke 3:1–14; Mark
          6:14–29
48, 49....Mark 1:14 to 2:17
50–52....Mark, chs. 11 to 14
52.......Mark 12:1–12
53.......Deut. 30:15

CHAPTER 5
55.......Shemoneh Esreh,
          First Benediction;
          Oesterley, p. 60
58.......Shemoneh Esreh,
          Eighth Benediction,
          Oesterley, p. 63

PAGES   CHAPTER 7
80.......Luke 17:26–30

CHAPTER 8
90, 91....I Cor. 1:18–24
92.......Isa. 40:3–5; Luke 3:
          4–6
92.......Luke 3:7–9
93.......Luke 7:18–28; 16:16;
          4:16–21
94.......Mark 2:1–17; 1:21–
          28
95.......Luke 7:18–23
96.......Mark 11:27–33
96.......Luke 11:15–20
97.......Luke 17:20–24
98.......Luke 12:54–56
98.......Isa. 40:29–31
100......Phil. 2:6–11

CHAPTER 9
103......Acts 15:36–41
105......Isa. 53:1–6
106......Matt. 4:3–11
107......Mark 6:2–5
108......Mark 8:27–33
109–111..Selections from
          Mark, chs. 14, 15

Acknowledgment is here made
of indebtedness to T. W. Pyms's
translation of the Gospel of
Mark and to the Choir Library,
Lafayette, Indiana.

PAGES CHAPTER 9—*Cont.*
112......Isa. 53:7–11
112, 113..John, ch. 21; Luke
          5:1–11
113......Mark 13:13
114......Rev. 5:12–14

CHAPTER 10
122–124..Rom., chs. 1 to 5

CHAPTER 11
128:......Shemoneh Esreh,
          First and Second
          Benedictions
129......I Peter 1:3–5; Col.
          1:12–14
130......Acts 15:16–18
131......Isa. 29:13; Mark 7:
          6, 7
131......Luke 18:10–14
132......Matt. 21: 28–31
132......Mark 10:42–45
133......Luke 15:3–7
134......Mark 8:34, 35; Luke
          14:28–30
135......Matt. 11:28–30;
          Luke 2:29–32
136......Luke 1:68–79

CHAPTER 12
144......Ps. 22
145......Mark 14:32–42;
          Mark 13:9–13
145, 146..Luke 6:20–23;
          I Peter 3:8–18

CHAPTER 13
152, 153..Ps. 2; Luke 14:26, 27
155......Mark 14:32–42
156......Matt. 10:24, 25
157......Rom. 8:35–39
158......I Cor. 11:23–26

PAGES CHAPTER 13—*Cont.*
158......Rev. 1:5, 6; I Peter
          5:10, 11

CHAPTER 16
184......Epistle to Barnabas,
          ch. 1
187......Jer. 21:8; Matt. 7:13,
          14
188......Matt. 4:17
189......Matt. 20:16; Luke
          18:14; Mark 9:35;
          10:15
189......Matt. 5:38–42
192......Mark 10:17–27
194......Luke 14:12–14
194......James 2:1–9; Matt.
          7:1–5
195......Matt. 7:1–5
196......Matt. 6:1–8; 23:1–
          12
197......Luke 15:11–32; Phil.
          2:5–11
198......I Clement, ch. 7

CHAPTER 18
208......Rom. 6:1–11
209......Col. 3–13; Matt. 6:
          14; Gal. 2:20; Mark
          11:25
212......I Peter 2:23, 24; Col.
          3:5–14
213......Luke 6:27–36
214......Matt. 6:19–24; 7:1;
          6:12
215......Matt. 5:38–42; 6:2–
          4
215......Matt. 18:21, 22
216......Matt. 5:23, 24
217......I Clement, ch. 13
218......Matt. 7:1–4
219......Matt. 18:23–35
220......Luke 6:20–23

PAGES   CHAPTER 19
223......Ex., chs. 7 to 14
224......The Book of Jonah;
          Matt. 8:18–27
225......Ps. 23
231, 232..Isa. 65:1–9
232, 233..Isa. 65:13–16; Luke
          6:20–22; 10:23, 24;
          I Cor. 2:9; Isa. 65:
          17–19

          CHAPTER 20
236, 237..I Clement, ch. 35;
          Prov. 4:18, 19
237......I Thess. 5:1–3
238......Isa. 13: 6–11
239......Mark 13:32; 9:1; 13:
          33–37
239......Luke 17:20–24; 10:
          17–24; Matt. 12:25–
          30
240......Luke 17:37
241......Luke 17:26–35
241......Eph. 5:14; Isa. 9:2
242......I Thess: 5:4–7
242, 243..Rom., ch. 5; I Cor.,
          ch. 15
243......Luke 9:62; I Clem-
          ent, ch. 11; Heb. 6:
          1–7; Luke 17:31; 9:
          57–62
244......Mal. 3:1; I Clement
          23:5; II Thess.
246......Luke 19: 11–27; I
          Clement 23:1–4;
          Hermas, Mandate V:
          1:1–6
247......II Clement 19:20;
          Rom. 5:1–5
248......Luke 17:7–10
249......Mark 14:32–42

PAGES   CHAPTER 22
265......I Clement 9:50
267, 268..Matt. 6:25–33; II
          Clement, ch. 20
269......Matt. 13:45, 46
270......Matt. 7:7, 8
271......Luke 12:2, 3, 6, 7
272......Matt. 7:9–11; 6:19–
          21
273......Matt. 6:24; 10:37,
          38
274......Luke 12: 4, 5; Luke
          6:43–45; Matt. 5:21,
          22
275......Matt. 5:27, 28
276......Matt. 5:33–37; 6:22,
          23
277......Matt. 6:2–4; 6:16–
          18
278......Luke 10:25–27
278......Hermas,
          Similitudes, 3

          CHAPTER 23
282......I Peter 2:6–10
283......Acts 10:34–43
283......Ps. 127:1
286......Origen, cf. James,
          Apocryphal New
          Testament

          CHAPTER 24
293......Eph., ch. 1; Rom. 11:
          33, 36
294......Rom. 12: 1, 2
296......Gal. 3:28
297......Col. 3:22–24
298......I Cor. 7:20–24
299......Luke 12:51–53; 6:5,
          Ms.D.
300......Luke 6:5, Ms.D.

PAGES   CHAPTER 24—*Cont.*   PAGES   CHAPTER 24—*Cont.*

301......Col. 3:18, 19; I Cor.   305......Matt. 7:24–27
        7:27–31; I Cor. 7:
        12–15   CHAPTER 25
302......Rom. 14:7–9   308......Matt. 7:7
303......Rom. 13:7, 8   309......Jer. 29:13
304......I Cor. 12:1–14   311, 312..Didache 9